OREGON TRAIL
1846

Compiled by J. Gildemeister Feb. 22nd, 1980

Legend:
- The Oregon Trail
- Sublette Cutoff
- Mormon Trail
- California Trail
- Barlow Road

ORGANIZED

MANDANS

SIOUX

TERRITORY

CHEYENNE

PAWNEE

UTE

Ft. Union

Ft. Pierre

Missouri River

Yellow R.

Musselshell R.

Big Horn R.

Tongue R.

Powder R.

Little

Stone R.

Belle Fourche R.

Cheyenne R.

White R.

Niobrara R.

James R.

Bighorn Mts

Rattlesnake Hills

Granite Mts

South Pass

Sweetwater

Split Rock

Devils Gate

Red Buttes

North Fork

Rock Independence

Laramie Peak

Ft. Laramie

Scotts Bluff

Chimney Rock

Platte

Laramie Mts

Laramie R.

DIVIDE BASIN

MOUNTAINS

St. Vrain's Fort

South Fork of Platte

Platte

Loup River

Ft. Kearney

Big Blue R.

Little Blue R.

Republican River

Kansas River

Council Bluffs

Missouri River

St. Joseph

Independence

Westport

Limited Edition

Rick Steber

Don Gray

Jerry Gildemeister

Drifting like summer clouds
  the wagons came and went;
We knew not where they came,
We knew not where they went.

1

The Bear Wallow Publishing Company
Union, Oregon

A Limited Edition Printing • 1980

© 1980 - The Bear Wallow Publishing Company
Copyright and Library of Congress Cataloging in Publication data on page *211*
ISBN-0-936376-02-3

Traces

Rick Steber   Don Gray   Jerry Gildemeister

NOTE

TRACES is composed of two parts. Beginning each of the seven chapters is the fictional account of the Nye family as told by Joe Nye. The remainder of each chapter is nonfictional narration written from interviews with our last living pioneers.

The purpose of the Nye story is to invest TRACES with a sense of continuity and to communicate in a personal way the hardships of a wagon journey. Although Joe Nye is an imaginary person he is a good example of the character it took to survive and build the west.

The nonfictional accounts of the pioneers, set apart by name and year of crossing, provide an insight into the past as seen from the present. This is oral history.

Included in TRACES is an Historical Note section (page 198), where the pioneers' photographs appear, accompanied by additional historical information about them and their families.

INTRODUCTION

Following Indian trails trappers were the first to cross the Rocky Mountains. In their footsteps came wagon emigrants attracted by free homestead land and the chance to begin life anew, out west, somewhere.

The wheels of these emigrant wagons carved the longest continuous road known in history, the Oregon Trail. Two thousand miles of wild desolate country was bridged with a rutted, rocky road. From the first crossing of the Oregon Trail by wagon in 1843 until the railroad and the automobile made the wagon obsolete, over a half million persons traveled the great highway west.

As the 20th century draws to a close the ruts of the Oregon Trail are still visible in stretches, but the number of individuals who made the wagon crossing and are alive to tell about it has dwindled to a small handful.

TRACES is a gathering of these last few pioneers. It is their story of the wagon trip as well as of life out west after they arrived. This then will be the final chapter, closing the Oregon Trail.

With the passing of the last pioneers any remembrance of the westward migration will be gone. And in the future the rutted road, so well traveled, will disappear. The Oregon Trail lost to time, plowed, paved, eroded by wind and rain — until we have no trace.

Jumping Off

simple thing — wind — can change a man.
I know, it changed Pa and blew us west.

The Kansas summer was unbearably hot, grain shriveled in the head and grass bleached a dried-out brown. Personally, I looked forward to fall and not just because of my birthday. Fall was a time when ducks returned to the pond and mosquitoes and flies died. Of course September also meant school and I most certainly did not relish the idea of being cooped up in a schoolhouse. Who would?

September came complete with Indian summer. The nights were cool and clear, the days the brightest blue and warm. But overnight that changed. A breeze came huffing across the rolling Kansas hills. It stripped the last yellow leaves and sent them flying from cottonwood trees. Following on the heels of the cold wind came snow. Round flakes hit the ground at a glancing angle.

The sudden weather change was good for only one thing — raising goose bumps. During the night Pa kept a fire roaring in the fireplace while the blizzard raged. In the morning when I got up there was a skift of powder snow on the floor, blown under the door.

"This can't possibly last," Pa said. "A freak storm is all."

Mother said it had come too early. Brother Willie and I didn't care a lick. We went out, built a snowfort, had a war.

The first snow of the year is fun, especially if it is unexpected. And this was unexpected. I do think Willie's dog Yellow had an inkling of impending snow because we found her curled in the haymow with only the tip of her nose sticking from the hay. We coaxed and coaxed and finally when Yellow could see that we would not leave her alone she came outside and played.

Day after tiresome day the storm blew on an east wind straight across Kansas. Low spots were filled with snow and high points were gashed to bare ground. Dust filled the air and breathing was accomplished through a bandana. On the inside of the barn, pie-shaped wedges of snow and dirt built higher, ever higher.

We became prisoners in our own house. Exposed wood turned the brunt of the gale but wind has a way of finding cracks. We spent our time huddled by the fire, listening to the oak wood snap and pop at the flames and watching Mother's kitchen curtains ripple with the movement of the inside air. The only exceptions to our constant sitting happened once in the morning and once in the afternoon — chores.

I milked the cow one week, Willie did the next. Odd man carried water. The routine was always the same; four buckets to the team, hogs two and a single to the hen house.

Even for me it was a burdensome chore but the last two pails, the ones to the house, had rewards. I would set the pails, ice clanking against the sides, on the back porch and Mother would stick her head out and call, "Here, Joe, have a hot oatmeal cookie," or "Care for some fresh bread with melted butter?" I liked that. Sometimes with raspberry jam.

Winter hung on forever, no letup to the cold and the wind never slowed. It raged. One evening after dinner Willie and I were lying on the floor in front of the fire. Mother was knitting in her rocking chair and Pa had been sitting at the table reading a letter from his brother when suddenly he stood and came to the fire. He got down on hands and knees and Willie and I thought at first he wanted to wrestle. He didn't. He just sat and stared into the fire.

When Pa did begin to speak the words that came from his mouth were like nothing we had heard him say before.

"Oregon — now that's the place to be. Waves off the ocean, the Pacific, break on her shores. And there is a valley called the Willamette where gardens grow year around. It never freezes in the Willamette. Watermelons for Christmas. Strawberry shortcake right now. And apples! Apples big as your head."

With that Pa reached over and rubbed Willie and my heads like he was shining them.

"When do we go?" I asked, excited at the possibility.

"Maybe one of these days," he said looking up in the direction of the rocking chair. "Maybe one of these days."

Pa was always a mild-mannered type, not given to excess and rarely a drinker. But one day he went to town and it was well after dark before he got back. He was quite awhile in the barn putting away the team and Mother sent me to check and make sure everything was all right. When I got to the barn Pa was lying in the hayloft singing a song about Oregon. I could tell he had been drinking.

"Sit down here for a minute, Joe," Pa told me and then got serious. "Kansas is no kind of life for us. What do we have here? Nothing. And you and your brother don't have a chance. What you need is opportunity and opportunity lies west.

"You remember your Uncle Elmo, don't you? That letter we got from him said there were more jobs than men to fill them. Work in the woods, farm, start a business of your own. They have a farm out of Albany, Oregon, and Elmo says it is just short of heaven."

When we went inside Mother put Pa to bed. She said he had come down with a case of stomach sickness.

More and more all the time Pa talked about Oregon. He interrupted conversations to introduce the subject.

"What does Kansas hold? Well, I'll tell you. Nothing. Nothing. Nothing. But now Oregon . . . ."

Spring brought with it wind, the same as winter's wind except warm and it sucked the last bit of moisture from the ground like a giant sponge.

The windmill began to pump only air and the stock pond turned mud hole. We had to haul water every few days with the team and wagon; four miles over to Mill Creek and from a hole Pa dipped water, two buckets at a time. He handed them to Willie and me and we dumped them into the thirty-gallon kegs in the back of the wagon. At home we reversed the procedure, Pa handing down buckets to us.

Our work horses were the finest team alive. They were roan, Pa was partial to roan, and we called them Dan and Charlie.

One day that spring Dan and Charlie were pulling the wagon toward Mill Creek. They leaned shoulder into the steady east wind and we just passed the old Ramsey place when Pa's hat blew off his head, jumped the pole fence and went rolling into a pile of brush. Pa was madder than a stirred hornet nest.

"This damn wind. This Goddamn wind," he said and that was strong language for a man who never cussed. He handed me the reins while he retrieved his black Dakota hat. As Pa climbed back onto the buckboard seat beside Willie and me he didn't say a word. I noticed the color of his face, red like a beet.

At the cutoff to the creek we didn't turn. Pa kept Dan and Charlie headed straight down the road toward town. Neither Willie nor I said a word.

In town Pa stopped behind the general merchandise store.

"Boys," he said, "I've got business to attend. Stay in the wagon and Willie, keep that dog with you."

We sat on the seat and waited for quite a spell. But after awhile we climbed in the back with Willie's dog. We went to sleep, Willie using Yellow for a pillow.

I awoke hearing Pa's voice and that of another man. Between the buckboard seat and the wagon I saw them. Evening shadows were long; I watched Pa unhitch Dan and then Charlie. The other man was holding a team of the ugliest white mules I ever saw. He exchanged with Pa and, holding the halter ropes to Dan and Charlie in one hand, he walked away. Pa began hooking the mules to our wagon.

"What is he doing?" Willie asked.

"Be quiet," I whispered.

When we reached the limits of town Willie and I crawled back on the seat with Pa, one on each side. Not a single word was said — just three pair of eyes stared ahead at the rumps of those ugly, spiteful mules. We met a man on the road; I felt embarrassed. Pa eventually broke the silence.

"I'm tired of scratching and never making a living here. You boys and your mother deserve better. And most of all, I'm tired of this damn-blasted wind. Joe and Willie, my boys, we are going to Oregon."

When he said that it was like a volcano had erupted. Willie, being the youngest, couldn't restrain himself.

"Yahoo!" he hollered at the top of his lungs and jumped to his feet. The mules, surprised, lurched ahead and Willie fell back in the seat.

"Pa?" Willie asked. "It's okay if Yellow goes along? She can go to Oregon. Can't she?"

"Sure."

The rest of the trip home was a dream. Pa talked about Uncle Elmo and how he had improved his Oregon farm. He said everything good that could be said about Oregon and he went on to explain we had to have mules to get there. I felt sorry for Dan and Charlie but Pa said there was no other way. The more Pa talked the less I despised the backsides of those mules.

We got home and I gave an extra measure of grain to the mules knowing what was in store. At the dinner table the subject of animals was never broached but I knew that Mother knew. And right after we finished eating Mother said it was time for bed. At a time like this? Who could sleep? It was Christmas Eve and Fourth of July rolled into one.

For a while Willie and I lay awake listening; in the other room Oregon was being discussed.

"But tell me why, Jackson, haven't I made this a home for you and the boys? All it amounts to is that you have talked yourself into Oregon. What makes you think it will be any better than Kansas?"

"It will be."

"You know it can't be heaven, the Bible says there is only one of those and that is in the sky, not west."

No one said anything for quite a spell. I could tell that Mother was crying and could hear her rocking chair going back and forth, back and forth.

And then with a tone of voice that was love Mother said, "Jackson, you might have gypsy blood running in your veins but we are a family. We live as one."

"Thank you," Pa said and then the light was blown out and the house grew quiet. I whispered something to Willie but he was already asleep; the word Oregon was on his lips.

The following day at school we told everyone we were leaving for Oregon. One girl I kind of liked, a little bit, cried and Jim, the best marble shot in the school, allowed me to win. I tried to give him back his black-eye shooter; he told me to keep it. "Give it a ride to Oregon." I put away his black-eye shooter in my trouser pocket and went home.

Mother had everything we owned sorted according to piles. The front room was covered with them; a pile for Willie, one for Pa and one for me. I had two pair of trousers, four favorite shirts, other necessary clothes including a jacket. In my pile I also had the saddlebags to the horse I was riding and a nosebag.

The one thing Mother insisted on taking was chickens. She said we had to have fresh eggs along the trail so Pa built a coop and nailed it on back of the wagon. Mother picked her eight best laying hens.

Looking the situation in the face honestly, we left behind more than we took. Some things I gave to my best friends. Then our last day came and went. It was Friday, three weeks before the end of school.

Saturday morning I was astride our saddle horse. Blaze was his name. He was a bay gelding with stockings on his hind feet and a blaze from his ears to his mouth. I was glad to be riding.

Willie sat in the wagon between Pa and Mother. There was a crowd to see us off, kids and people the folks knew. The wagon started forward, I trailed.

"Look out for Indians," someone called as warning.

"Watch it when you cross rivers," came another. That was the first time I had thought about dangers. Now it was there, stuck in my mind. Danger.

Near the top of the ridge I let the wagon go ahead. It broke over the other side; I stopped, looked back. There was a small cluster of people, like bees on a drop of honey, and behind them was our barn that would hear no munching tonight and our house that would not be warmed by fire.

I waved, headed Blaze west, never looked back.

Grace and I were the spitting image of each other. Both eight years old we could have been twins, but Grace was a Fitzgerald and I am a Jones, Mabel Jones from Hayes County, Nebraska.

Through the first and second grades we girls walked each other to and from school every day. Then came a morning when I was a potful of excitement and boiling over.

"Grace, Grace," I called and when my best friend got there I threw my arms around her. "Guess what? We're moving west. Dad said so last night."

Not until I saw the look on her face did I perceive the consequence of what I had said. We were leaving. Grace and I would be parting.

My parents allowed a certain amount of latitude with us children but the Fitzgeralds were another matter. For instance, Grace could not have a doll of her own. Her mother had even made her promise not to play with mine.

Jones children had only one iron-clad rule to live by, "Play when chores are done." There was never an exception to the rule and as it came closer to the time for us to leave there were more chores than ever to do. That left precious little time for Grace and me but we usually got together just before the sun went down. She came to our place or I went there. We played in back.

From the day I first told Grace that we were going west there was a distance between us. It was almost as if I had left in spirit.

At home one evening Mother told us to set out everything we wanted to take. We were down to the final stages of loading and according to Mother, weight was the prime consideration. Brother Alma had to dump half his marbles, Lawrence had to pick a single favorite rock. When my turn came Mother told me one doll was plenty.

The problem with taking one doll was that I had two, a china doll and a rag doll. I loved them equally well but the china doll had belonged to Mother. I took the rag doll with me out to play and gave it to Grace.

"Mom would never let me have it."

"Don't tell your mother. Hide my doll in the willows. Make a home for her and when you play, think about me way out west somewhere."

It was pretty emotional to give away a doll but if I had to leave her behind I wanted her to be with the best friend I will ever have, Grace.

Dad had the wagon set to go. He built cupboards with big doors on the back of the wagon and a frame bed inside the bows. I helped him stretch the canvas cover and tie off the rope.

On the morning we pulled out of Hayes County, Nebraska, there was a small surprise for each of us three children. It was a gift from the folks for being good. I got an autograph book, blue in color and just right for a pocket.

I waited for Grace, wanting her to be the first to sign my book.

"Please, then I'll always have something to remember you by."

"Okay," Grace said, "but you have to promise. Do you promise?"

"Sure, I do."

"Say it."

"I promise. Okay, what did I promise?"

"That," she said, "you will not read what I write until after you have dinner tonight."

Grace took the autograph book away and I saw her writing something at our kitchen table that had no chairs around it.

Dad started our team of horses, Flax and Floss, and the wagon pulled away. Grace returned my autograph book at the last possible second. She ran along behind and handed it to me. I was stretched out on the bed reaching back as far as I could.

For just an instant we grabbed hands. Tears were streaming down her face, she was so sad, and then Grace was gone, lost in a sea of running children. They dropped away one by one until not a soul was near our wagon. We were completely alone.

We stopped after a long day's drive. Dad unhitched the team, watered and rubbed them down. They were tired and relieved not to be pulling.

Dad dug a hole for a fire and once he had it going he hung the iron kettles so Mother could start cooking. We all helped. By the time dinner was over the sun was down and it was growing dark.

I went to get the autograph book from its hiding place under the quilts and sat down out in the open, away from the wagon.

Turning to catch the light from the campfire I read:

"When you get old and ugly
Like young folks tend to do,
Remember your friend Grace
Is old and ugly, too."

His name was James Barton, my father. He was a great worker and had two children at the home in Wamego, Kansas. We lived as sharecroppers with Father farming another's land.

One harvest there was a serious argument concerning the crop split. The owner wanted more than Father had agreed to pay. There was a gun pulled and a shot fired.

At the time I was but a babe in my mother's arms. She and I and brother Leon were down to the store when we heard the news. A man came charging in hollering details. He had no idea we were there.

"The newcomer, at the other end of town, well he done flew mad and shot James Barton through the stomach. I think he is gonna die."

"I knew that fellow was a hot-head from the start. He . . .," said a farmer in a straw hat, then looked at Mother and stopped in mid-sentence. He saw her face. We tore out the front door and Mother ran the length of town to the field. By then Father was dead.

During those trying times a relative of ours, Aunt Jo Skinner, became close friends with Mother. They talked and talked, claimed there was no future for them in Wamego, Kansas, and decided to pack their children and go west.

The two women pulled together three wagons and took Leon, me and a boy Aunt Jo Skinner was raising, Nye Burnett. Before we left they hired two old men to do roustabout work and help drive.

When the Barton-Skinner three-wagon outfit pulled out we had everything we owned with us. Loose stock was scattered behind, dogs and beef and an old milk cow we called Bessie brought up the rear.

Our family moved around a lot, Dad was a roamer. He always thought there was a better place just down the road. We tried a homestead in Colorado but after a couple of years gave it up and went back to Missouri. The family by then numbered three children, twin boys George and John being born in Colorado, and Mother pregnant again.

It took two weeks to return by wagon and the horses were in such poor health that on hills Mother helped push. All across the plains it was mud, mud, mud, and when Dad stopped to give the horses a rest Mother would catch up and find a stick to clean her shoes.

That winter a baby boy was born and during the next two years there were two more. That made six of us children and Dad constantly had us on the move. We wound up back in Colorado and Mother and Dad both took jobs. Dad worked as a farmhand for a dollar a day while Mother got the same pay for cooking and housekeeping. She worked two months, long enough to earn sixty dollars for a milk cow. She thought milk was important. We made butter by rolling cream in a half-gallon fruit jar and existed on bread, butter and milk.

Sometime before spring Mother received a letter from her sister telling that she and her husband were living in Elgin, Oregon. She wrote glowingly about what a wonderful place it was — sawmills, and plenty of work for everyone. This time it was Mother who wanted to move. Dad jumped at the chance. I thought the trip would be a lark.

Several weeks before we left a burro wandered into our place. He was old and had evidently been turned loose from a pack string to graze on the ditch banks. We sort of adopted him and gave him the name Ned.

Ned was our pet. He was gray in color and stubborn as the day is long. Somehow we convinced Dad that we should take Ned to Oregon with us, suggesting that some of us older kids could take turns riding and save our team in that way. Dad always listened to logic; he went and paid fifty cents a hoof to have Ned shod.

On the first day of March 1900 we left Monte Vista, Colorado, with a heavy wagon and a light spring wagon. My brother John and I were supposed to have the first two rides on Ned. John was first and by the time we were out of the valley Ned and John were a long way behind. I split the difference between the wagon and Ned since I did not want to miss my turn.

A burro has one gait — slow — and there is no way to make it hurry. I waited for John. The wagon went on ahead. We both walked and tried to coax more speed from Ned. John got in front and pulled on the reins as hard as he could. He put them over his shoulder and really leaned his weight. I stood behind swatting Ned on the rump with a switch. For all our effort we did not gain any additional speed from Ned. He held slow and steady.

The wagon had long since passed over the horizon and John and I started to discuss our situation. Neither of us knew the way to Oregon, we had nothing to eat and no way to stay warm. I was the one who pulled the bridle off old Ned and we started to run in the direction of the wagon. Mile after mile, John and I were exhausted when we finally caught sight of the wagon. It was several more hours before we were riding.

And as we sat on the tailgate eating dust I looked back, thought about Ned. He was out there somewhere I knew, with no bridle to hinder him, naked as the day he was born. Except for his shoes — fifty cents apiece.

God, was Dad ever mad.

On the Road

After the first few days of travel Blaze and I were both pretty well broke to the trail. Willie and Yellow did not fare as well; the pads on Yellow's front feet bled and Willie's upper lip, where he licked, cracked under the intensity of the sun.

I felt sorry for my younger brother and gave him turns riding Blaze and I walked. Being on the ground felt good at times, it allowed blood to return to places it hadn't been getting.

The countryside we passed never varied. We could have been just over the ridge from our old place; the hills and draws looked familiar. Eventually I came to the conclusion that all Kansas is poured from the same mold.

Where there was water you could generally count on someone living and before our mules were allowed to drink Pa would always ask permission. Sometimes between houses there could be quite some distance and after being caught short once Pa always made sure the water barrel was leveled off.

We filled at Blue River and Little Blue and then for days we were either climbing or descending. Hills, hills, up and down all the time and then we hit Nebraska, wide-open, flat-as-a-table Nebraska. The Platte River wove back and forth to the north of the trail and from the backwaters and sloughs clouded millions of mosquitoes. Mornings and evenings the air was so thick I wore a bandana so as not to breathe in mosquitoes.

The weather held good until early one afternoon thunderheads mushroomed. Willie crawled inside the wagon just before it rained.

"Willie, be sure and don't touch the cover," Pa called back, " 'cause if you do the canvas is going to leak."

Through the partially opened back flap I watched Willie shake water from his sleeve. The rain kept coming in a downpour, the top layer of gumbo mud became slick. Finally, near a small grove of cottonwood Pa called it quits, said we would make camp for the day.

Pa took care of the mules while I staked Blaze and helped Willie take the sheet metal camp stove from the box of the wagon. We gathered twigs and sticks around the trees and Pa struck a fire. For Mother's convenience Pa set the grub box near the fire and we strung a tarp so that Mother would not get wet cooking. I lay under the wagon, leaned against my saddle, and watched Mother peel potatoes and carrots. The skins I took and split between the mules and Blaze.

The sun was beginning to set on the flat skyline when the storm lifted and exposed the westward horizon. If I ever saw a more beautiful sight I don't know what it would be: the sun, a big yellow ball, balanced on the flatness of the Platte River, trees just budding green and thousands upon thousands of cranes overhead. The large birds flew in a V-formation like geese and in loud squawking voices they continually talked to one another.

And then the sun was gone, the colors dropped to shades of gray and the cranes found an island on the river and were quiet.

That night Willie and I slept beneath the wagon like we usually did. We were warm and dry with the only discomfort being the smell of Yellow. Willie's dog was wet and smelled to high heaven, but Willie loved his dog and I had to endure its closeness.

The next morning the sun shone, forgetting about the vicious rainstorm of yesterday and by noon the ground was cracked and looked as if it had never seen a drop of moisture.

We made the acquaintance of a family man living in a sod house and farming the river bank. He told us to be careful. The river, he said, was lousy with quicksand and I especially was careful because I didn't want to lose Blaze and have to start walking.

Mother, although she always took care of herself, was not in the same condition as she was the first few days of traveling. Gone was the dress, and in its place Mother had sewn bloomers. She wore a bonnet and was ever mindful of her appearance. A looking glass was suspended from one of the wagon bows. Occasionally she would interrupt its constant swaying motion to examine her face. Willie and I would never do such a thing. Who cared how we looked? Anyway, we wore hats twenty-four hours a day, our hair never needed combing.

The terrain on the cutoff between the South Platte and North Platte was dry and hilly. Deep gullies cut in all directions and the trail kept to ridgetops wherever possible. This region was different from the flat river bottom where at anytime I had been able to look back and see the previous night's camp. Plants reflected the harsh landscape. They were unfriendly, with thorns, needles and blades of grass that cut like a knife. Here on the steep grades was sand and it made the going twice as tough for our mules — which by then we had taken to calling White and Off-White.

Willie and Mother walked a majority of the distance and sometimes I traded off and let Willie ride Blaze and I walked. Mother never did ride, she disliked big animals. But she did like small animals and as she walked she talked to Yellow as often as she did Willie and me.

Even though he was ten I am sure Mother considered Willie still to be her baby. She was protective of him but the farther we went the more independent Willie became. The wagon trip seemed to mature Willie, he became more confident of himself.

To a boy from Kansas the geography of North Platte was a different planet. The wide sandy river bottom was hemmed in by bluffs and broken rolling hills dry as a bone.

The weather — frying pan hot, and dust to choke a mule; even the wild sunflowers shriveled in the heat. And from this description of hell rose the shapes of two gigantic rocks — Courthouse and Jail Rock. They were landmarks off in the distance but I could tell they were huge. We did not detour south off the Oregon Trail to inspect the famous rocks as I would have liked. We camped near a town and I asked Pa if I could ride over for a look. He said no, that I had to save Blaze.

That evening I dreamed of touching cool rock and climbing to the highest point of Courthouse Rock. I wondered if from there I could possibly see the Rocky Mountains.

"I see it. I see it," Willie hollered. The canvas cover was rolled back and Willie stood on the rail in order to view Chimney Rock. That was the landmark Pa had read about numerous times in the emigrant guide book and for weeks we looked forward to spotting the rocky shaft. When we arrived Pa said we were roughly one-third of the way to Willamette Valley, Oregon.

Flies and mosquitoes hung thick close to the North Platte. We camped that evening in the shadow of the rocky needle. The stars came out bright and Pa, by firelight, read one more time how the spire was shortened some thirty feet by soldiers practicing with a cannon. A lot of pioneers, the guide said, carved their names in the soft sandstone of Chimney Rock but it went on to warn that the rock was continually sloughing. The area was to be considered dangerous. Again, I did not get to inspect the carved names and oh, but it would have been nice to have laid over a day. That would have given me time to explore.

We kept moving at a steady pace; finally at Scotts Bluff, the most impressive sight by far, we took a day. In the morning Willie and I had to bring in driftwood from the river bank so Mother would have a fire for washing clothes and baking. And we had to help hang clothes, so it was afternoon before we rode Blaze double in the direction of the pass.

On the way up the fingers of a wash, prickly pears and wild sage grew and in a small opening I spotted the shell of a petrified turtle. Willie got down to hand it to me and he almost stepped on a rattlesnake. The wash was thick with snakes so we rode on, trusting Blaze to know where and where not to step.

The sun began to set behind the massive cliffs of sandstone that is Scotts Bluff. There was plenty of daylight remaining but we were blocked from the sun by the imposing walls. With the cooler shadow air I thought it safe to walk and we reached the summit with a steady climb. From the top we could look ahead at the trail we would be traveling the next few days. Out there the yellow sunlight was still shining.

"Hey, Joey," called Willie, "come over here and look at what I found."

Willie had discovered a freshly dug grave. Moisture was still in the stark white sand. Stamped on the mound with the print of a small hand was the single word, "Grandma."

"I wonder how come they didn't roll a rock for a tombstone? Why didn't they do that?" Willie asked.

"I guess," I said, standing and looking around, "Scotts Bluff is monument enough."

The following morning we broke camp early and when we topped Mitchell Pass the grave was still in shadow. I rode over, took a look. The wind during the night had obliterated "Grandma." The grave looked old.

The road toward Fort Laramie was soft and sandy and hung fairly close to the North Platte River. The going became slow and the mules worked for every mile we added. Scattered alongside the road were heavy items discarded by other emigrants years before; cast iron stoves lay rusting and brass bedsteads were twisted, having been trampled by stock. There were wagons and wagon parts scattered here and there, left to weather.

At the river crossing a large number of half-naked Indians were congregated. If the fort hadn't been right there we all would have been scared but as it was we proceeded through the Indians and stopped inside the fort in front of the officers' quarters. The grounds were open and nearly everywhere were Indians. They outnumbered the soldiers. And beside our wagon a halfbreed scout and a soldier set up a game for a group of the young Indian boys. The soldier placed a stick on the ground and any boy who could hit it with his arrow was given a chunk of hardtack.

As unaccustomed as we were to Indians Pa did not wish to stay near the fort. We bought what few provisions we needed at the Sutler's Store: butter, dried pumpkin, jerked beef, salt and hardtack. The butter we had started the trip with, packed in the flour sack, had melted in the flour but made dandy shortcakes and the fresh butter we again stowed in the flour sack.

Ahead from Fort Laramie the Rocky Mountains stood, waiting to be crossed, and their presence soon became known. Laramie Peak was a small, hazy blue bump on the horizon that grew larger and larger until I wondered why it was not called a mountain instead of a peak. And to think Laramie Peak is not even part of the Rockies. They must be something!

Coming west from Monte Vista,
Colorado, we had to rustle for anything we
got. There was usually grass for the horses,
though Dad carried grain along just in case.
And there were times we made dry camp so we
kept both water barrels full.

Most nights we camped near water and the
night in particular I am thinking about we were
camped on the shore of a lake with several other
wagons. After dinner Dad was glassing the far side
of the lake with field glasses when he spotted
a bear.

"When I shoot that bear," Dad said, picking up his muzzle-loading shotgun, "there is going to be meat for everyone."

The loads he made extra heavy, maybe five inches of powder and shot, and he tamped them down tight. The gun had two hammers; one barrel was smooth, the other was choke. The hammer on the choke barrel was worn to the point that even a jar might set it off. On account of that Dad always touched the choke barrel first.

We watched Dad as he made his way around the lake, easing up on the bear. But I guess the bear had been shot at before because he let Dad get only so close — barely out of range and then the bear would take off, run for a ways and stop. Well, Dad came back pretty dejected and hung his shotgun on loops from the wagon bows.

The following day we were coming across a flat and Dad spotted a sage hen sitting on a rock outcropping. He was anxious to get meat — we had been without for several days. We stopped and Dad reached back and got that old shotgun. In case he might miss with the first shot he pulled back both hammers.

BOOM! He pulled the choke trigger first and it was like a dynamite explosion. The force kicked him, skinned the side of his face and cracked the shotgun stock.

"God blame!" he said, pulling himself to a sitting position. "I forgot that had bear loads."

I went to have a look at the sage hen. All I found was feet and feathers — nothing more.

Four brothers died in infancy and then we lost Mother to pneumonia. "Five graves are enough," Dad said. "We won't stay in such a damn country that takes away all those we love."

My oldest brother Will married a girl and for a while they lived in our home. She tried to be mother to six children, the youngest nine-month-old Flo, but it didn't work. After a few months she and Will moved from under our roof.

I took over for Will. What he had done, I did. I was a girl of twelve but I milked the cows, fed the pigs, did all the outside work. My oldest sister Mary was just the opposite — she took care of the house and watched Flo.

Dad was serious about leaving Illinois and one cool evening, just before midnight, we pulled out. I rode our saddle horse, a dapple gray named Sambo. Dad drove one wagon loaded with springs and mattresses and all the kids. Bill Jinks, a neighbor friend, brought up the rear with our hack. He carried supplies and household goods.

Bill was a young man about thirty and more like a brother. He played games with us and agreed to come because he thought he might be able to help. He did not really want to leave Illinois.

After the first day we fell into a routine. The kids climbed in and out of the wagon while it was moving and spent the day picking up twigs and firewood, throwing them in the wagon. I helped harness and unharness the teams and I, by myself, took care of Sambo. We bought milk and eggs from farms we passed — the eggs, I think, ran twenty cents a dozen — other food we carried with us or bought in towns. At night we camped and sister Mary cooked a hot meal in the skillet.

The routine was always the same, no variation until we reached St. Louis, Missouri. We had told our friends back home that we would stop there and pick up mail and when we did Mary had a letter from her boyfriend back in Effingham, Illinois. He said to come home and marry him — Dad put her on the train.

I suppose we could have taken the train west from St. Louis, we had money after Dad sold our farm, but traveling by wagon was the spirit of the times. And besides, Dad would never sell his team of horses — not unless he absolutely had to. They were a matched team of iron grays — one mare, one stallion — registered Copper Bottom.

On the outskirts of St. Louis we pulled into a little park. While we camped there Dad said that we had to lighten the load or the horses would never make it. He was right — even though I was haying and graining them every night they were going downhill. The kids set out doll furniture and clothes, keeping only dolls. And Dad removed the household goods, even the crib that had held all eleven of his children. He was sentimental about the crib but we left it there in the park and headed out with food and bedding, the wagon and hack stripped to nothing.

Coming across Missouri, Bill Jinks got so homesick he couldn't eat and one morning he and Dad went for a walk away from the fire. When they returned Dad paid Bill for what he had done and took him to the train depot. After that I gave up riding Sambo and drove the hack.

An uncle lived in Missouri and Dad thought we might buy a farm there. The uncle was Mother's brother and he owned 640 acres of what he called bottomland but when we got there all it amounted to was swampland. There were so many tree knees sticking up out of the water that a deer could walk from one to another and never get his feet wet.

While we were there we cooked over a campfire beside the house. Then our hound dog died. I think it was the heat and humidity in the air. After he was buried Dad said, "If this country is so bad that a hound dog can't live, I'm not about to subject you children to it."

We moved on, heading west. One day Dad ran into a friend. He had been a captain in the Union army and he and Father had fought on the same side. His name was Osgood and he held construction contract on the first railroad through the Cherokee strip. He offered Dad a job.

We spent a long cold winter on the Oklahoma plains, living in tents. Without the generosity of engineers who threw coal to us I don't think we could have possibly survived.

So in March of 1900 we left Monte Vista, Colorado, with two teams and wagons. Along the way Dad shot our dinner. He had an old muzzle-loading shotgun and killed so many rabbits we had them running out our ears. It was rabbit every meal.

Mother cleaned and cooked the rabbits and made pones of bread in a long-handled fry pan. Another of her chores was washing. Every week she built a fireplace out of stones and set the smoke-black tub over it, washing on a rub board with dried, homemade soap. All of us children got in the act hanging clothes over brush. In some places where the brush was scattered we might have clothes spread for a quarter mile drying in the sun.

All of us old enough to walk, walked. We went barefooted, saving our shoes for when we got to Oregon. Since I was thirteen with five younger brothers and sisters, I was second mother. One of my nightly duties was to make up the beds in the wagons. The boys slept in the light wagon and we girls in the other. Mother and Dad slept on the ground.

We had come into Utah and had not seen a single Indian until late one afternoon as I was making the beds a chill ran up my spine. I turned around and not more than five or six feet away was an Indian buck, wrapped in a blanket and sitting on a horse. I was scared, and for a moment thought I might lose my footing and fall off my perch on the brake shoe. The brave saw I was frightened — he grinned, then rode away leaving me to wonder if he had been there at all.

The following day we saw two more Indians at a distance and when evening came we made camp in a nice broad flat that had a stream running through it. A string of wagons came into view and the wagonmaster rode ahead to our camp. He said he was amazed we were traveling alone and asked if we had had Indian trouble. He said we were in Indian country.

Forty-two wagons camped beside us that night and their presence made our horses nervous. They left the next morning while we were getting ready for breakfast. As they pulled out brother George got kicked by one of our horses. The shoes cut his face to pulp and bone protruded from his jaw.

I was so shocked and scared for George. In the distance the wagon train bound for California went its merry way. They never knew our trouble.

We swung off the Oregon Trail in Wyoming making our way north while Dad asked about work. Work was scarce.

One night somewhere in Montana an old miner shared our camp. After dinner Mother decided to get out a few rocks she had collected and let the miner tell her what they were. Mother was always collecting rocks along the way. She hunted and saved pretty ones. When Father found them he threw them away, so Mother resorted to secret hiding places in the wagon.

The old miner examined each rock carefully, rolling them in his hands. He never displayed any real interest until he came to a piece of white quartz. He stared at flecks of dull yellow. ''Where did you find this rock?'' he asked.

For the life of her, Mother could not remember — she had no idea. The miner verbally retraced our steps along the trail. Still she could not remember.

In the morning the miner was off, in the opposite direction. He was looking for gold and we were left trying to get a mile closer to Oregon.

The top buggy was the unusual thing about our crossing. As far as I ever heard we are the only ones who ever brought a top buggy all the way. We were known far and wide because of it.

We left out of Nebraska with thirteen head of horses, two wagons and that top buggy. My brother, five years older, drove one wagon; Father drove the other and Mother drove the top buggy with her sister riding along for company. I crossed on Logan, a nice little four-year-old gelding.

The buggy was black and the top the same color. There was a single seat and we used a team of horses to pull, we had to because the ruts in the Oregon Trail were worn so deep that a horse by himself would be stuck up there on the island.

The top buggy went first in order to keep out of the dust, but Mother made a lot of stops. Whenever we came across the site of a grave — and we were always coming across graves — Mother would rearrange the rocks, piling them up so the loose stock wouldn't trample them. If there was any kind of wooden marker like a cross or a board with a name, she would set it upright and pile rocks to hold it that way.

When Mother was done she would catch up to us. She never got too far behind. She was afraid of being left out there alone.

There came a time when my folks could see no future in Goodland, Kansas. Friends wrote to us about prospects in Oregon; they said there was no place like it. I was four years old when we packed and left Kansas.

Father took others' advice and traded our work team for a pair of mules. When he brought them home Mother cried. She was scared to death that they would never make it.

We traveled in company of my grandparents, two uncles and one family of friends. There were a lot of times when one of them could not make it up a grade and our mules would have to go back and help pull. They had horses.

The trip to Oregon, from my four-year-old standpoint, was fun. My brother Percy and I played in the wagon. Father took the canvas down in the daytime so we could see out and put it back over the bows at night. When we passed through towns we stopped and added supplies, but for Mother there was little to look forward to. She did the cooking, washing and baking.

Only once on the trip did Mother spank me and then she had every right. It came about when we went to lay over a day so she could bake bread. Father started a fire in the cook stove, but when Mother went to raise the dough she couldn't find the yeast cakes. I had eaten every last one.

I got switched with a stick — oh boy — and didn't sit down for a month of Sundays.

My grandmother Lawrence had a nice little saddle pony she was fond of riding. When she had a mind to she rode him, otherwise her horse trailed behind the wagon. A day came, though, when their team broke down. One fell sick and Grandfather asked if he could hitch the saddle horse. Grandmother could not refuse because it meant they would either slow us all down or they would drop behind.

Grandmother said, ''My little bay might have to do the dirty work, but he won't have my weight added. I will walk.'' She stepped down from the wagon and walked the rest of the way.

Unannounced Company

West of Fort Laramie was rough country, draws and broken flats to cross. It was dry, dust hung permanently in the air and the only color save tan and brown was the dark green of yucca plants. Yucca grows best in the very worst spots.

Into this barren landscape, cutting our path at an angle, rode an old man on a mustang and trailing a loose pack mule. He wore a bright red flannel shirt even though it was the hot part of the day and as we drew alongside he called, '' 'Bout time to think of a place to stop. You folks mind if I put up near you this evening?''

Pa told him to fall in behind and for the next mile or two he rode alone, oblivious to the dust cloud.

His mustang looked in good shape but on the downhill side of twenty. The saddle on her back was a relic but not anywhere near as old as the gentleman who straddled it. He wore a pair of buckskin britches to contrast his shirt and his white hair and beard were so bushy all that could be seen of a face were two patches of skin around the eyes and a long, angular nose.

I dropped back to talk and see what he was doing out alone on the plains. But for a while we just rode side by side, silently, me choking on the dust. The country seemed to be a mirror of the old man; the back of his hands and neck were sunbaked, cut by ravines.

"We're going to Oregon," I finally blurted and he looked over, glad that the silence was broken.

"My name is Cal. What's yours?"

"Joey Nye."

"Joey, they call me Cal with due respect for the great state of California. That is the place. Oregon — no, it rains too much there. California — why with all that sunshine you don't have to plant a garden, you just stand at the back door, throw a handful of seeds and the garden takes care of itself.

"If you want, tell your pa to veer south. I know of a good spot to camp, there's a trickle of water and plenty of feed."

The trickle Cal knew about was barely that. We dug a hole in a wet spot and waited for it to fill. Before the stock drank Mother dipped a coffee pot of water.

"I apologize, Mr. Cal, for the muddy taste," Mother said, serving a cup to the old man.

"Ma'am, I've seen it too thick to drink and too thin to plow. This suits me fine, thank you."

After dinner was over and the fire built back we sat around talking. Cal told of his days spent traveling.

"Came to California 'cause I had nothing better to do. I've done it all in my time; caught a case of gold fever — only cure I ever heard for that was a pick and shovel. I moved enough gravel and the fever broke.

"No sir, that wasn't for me. I drifted around and went back to leading wagon trains over the Rockies. That was all I did. I'd bring a train out and then turn around and head east until I found others who needed my services. They paid good money, I might add.

"I've been in Philadelphia for a few years but that's no kind of life. I want to spend my last days in sunny California."

"Boys, it's time for bed," Mother said and her voice was a surprise, I had forgotten she was around.

Willie and I crawled under the wagon and lay down in the pile of quilts. The last I saw of Cal before I went to sleep was his figure bent over the campfire adding little twigs. The light was bright and then died down, camp was quiet. Coyotes in the distance took up yipping at a coming full moon.

The following day Cal kept up with us and he and I rode side by side. Willie walked when he wanted and rode in the wagon when he didn't. And all the while the old man in the buckskin britches talked on and on.

"Up ahead is the Dry Sandy. Not a tree in sight, scarce as teeth in a hen's mouth." Cal paused, took out a pipe, loaded and lit it before he continued. "One time I was bringing seventy wagons through there. A boy and an old man were coming along, the boy was driving. But they got into an argument, the boy got shot. I don't remember what started the quarrel, maybe money, all I know was the end result. The old man killed the boy.

"We gave him a fair trial. The vote said he should hang but we were without a tree in sight. I gave the command to push three wagons together and we made a tripod out of the tongues. We hung the old man then and there."

As Cal told stories of his comings and goings over the Oregon Trail I studied him out of the corner of my eye. He always hunched over the saddle horn like his shoulders were heavy and stared intently at the dust coming up from the rear wagon wheels. He looked tired, old, and I hoped that he lived long enough to be buried in the land he loved, California.

" . . . tried my hand at trapping one spring, down in Great Salt Lake country. Snow was head high to a tall Indian, chinook on the way and I was pickin' up my line. Above a series of rapids was an ol' snag I tied off on and as I came and peeked around, the biggest beaver alive was looking me hard in the eye. Maybe a foot away, and as far as size went he looked like a grizzly b'ar. We both froze for a second and then he swapped ends, slapped me a time or two alongside the head with his tail and disappeared. Now I knew he couldn't have pulled loose of a trap and I was right. Still in the jaws was his front left foot, he had chewed his leg off.''

As a throwback to his trapping days Cal carried a Green River knife in a sheath, a possibles bag and a Hawken rifle, although the Hawken was outdated.

''This Hawken saved my life more times than I can remember . . . I'll have to tell one on myself. It was coming dusk and I had the wagons circle beside a lake. I took midnight guard and before I could settle down I spotted something hugging the brushy shoreline. We were in Blackfoot country and I was wary. A fog moved in, made whatever it was hard to see in the moonlight. Finally I hollered, 'Halt or I'll shoot.' There was no answer and for a minute the figure stopped dead in its tracks. But then it started moving again. The closer it got the more it looked to be an Indian crawling along on all fours. I called out one more warning, my Hawken went to my shoulder and I don't remember lifting it. There was a flash before my eyes and I saw the outline of the Indian pitch forward head first in the lake. The rest of the night the camp was in turmoil, the women expecting any minute to be attacked and killed. In the morning a group of us men went to have a look at the Indian. He was right there where I had shot him, hadn't moved a muscle — only the body was the body of a timber wolf. He had a brown coat, white belly and an exploded heart. It took me quite awhile to live that down. One of the boys told me next time to save my ammunition until I could get downwind and smell if it was Indian.''

Cal continued to travel slowly and stay with us. He could have made better time on his own but I think he secretly enjoyed leading our wagon train of one. And he was a blessing to have along; he knew the way, the best spots to camp and his friendliness with me especially, but also with Willie, Yellow, Pa and Mother, helped to shorten the miles.

At the last crossing of the North Platte Pa had planned to ferry but Cal claimed that would be a waste of money. He said that he had crossed many a wagon at Red Buttes without anyone having to get wet. Then Cal laughed, ''But everyone gets wet at Red Buttes. That is the last we see of the North Platte. It will be safe to cross, take my word for that.''

Red Buttes was just as Cal said it would be, a safe gravel crossing at a bend in the river and the landscape nearby was unusual to say the least. There were both soft and brilliant shades of red, green and tan. We climbed through these colors going away from the North Platte drainage and the route was long and hot. There were mineral springs and a lake Cal said was poison. The mules weren't the least bit interested, but Blaze would have taken a drink if I had let him.

The ground we passed was poor, sage was stunted and then we came over a hill and the whole country opened.

"Those are the Sweetwater Mountains," said Cal. "You will enjoy the Sweetwater. I never met a man who didn't."

With that Cal patted me on the back.

"Lake ahead, don't get excited, though," Cal told Pa and Mother. "It's Alkali Lake, even smells bad. But the Sweetwater River and Independence Rock aren't far. We can camp there if you like."

The dry barren landscape between the North Platte and Sweetwater rivers was like a purging. We worked it from our systems; then ahead I saw the spot mentioned by every emigrant who crossed the Oregon Trail — Independence Rock. To me it gave the appearance of a stone heart lying on top of the ground. Worn and cracked, the piece of granite looked out of place with the sage, but then the Sweetwater River which curled around one corner of the giant rock was also out of place. For the first time in a long time there was plenty of feed for the mules, the mustang and Blaze.

After we made camp and were waiting for dinner Cal came over to where I was killing a rattlesnake and said, "Follow me. I got something to show you." We left Willie playing with Yellow near the base and climbed the rock hump. There were names carved everywhere, some more elaborately done than others. Most bore a personal touch of the signer. It was amazing how many carved where they were from, "Kansas," "Illinois," "Ohio," as if where they were from was important.

Cal led the way to the top of the rock and from there we could see in all directions, see where we had been and where Cal said we would go. West looked closed by rugged country but Cal said it would open. And then he showed me something special, a certain section of Independence Rock where he had written, "Cal," and recorded each year he had passed this way. Most of the dates were in the '40s and '50s. There were twelve separate years listed. Cal took his pocket knife and began year thirteen. Below that he carved a straight line in the rock.

"I don't figure on passing this way again," he said. "I might just as well finish. Why don't you sign beside me?"

I did, etching, "Joe Nye — Oregon Bound."

The rugged country west of Independence Rock opened with the road passing a divide near Devils Gate. The Sweetwater River had cut a notch in solid rock and the river valley on the west side made it seem like a gate to heaven. The Sweetwater ran gently in a long valley with plenty of grass growing on the flat near the river; sharp outlines of mountain and rough country stood silhouetted in the afternoon sun.

But the valley was both a blessing and a curse. We had plenty of grass along with rattlesnakes and frequent crossings of the Sweetwater River. We crossed so many times I lost count.

The worst part of it was finding out we were climbing toward the Continental Divide and I did not even know it until Cal announced, "Away from the river and a steady pull will top the Rockies. From there ain't goin' to be much of anything. If you cut some hay and top the water barrel now you will be glad later on that you did."

The climb over the backbone of the Rockies was long and exhausting, a drain on man and beast. We walked, except for Pa who drove the wagon. The higher we climbed the harder it became to breathe until it seemed my lungs were on fire. I held onto Blaze's tail and let him pull.

Rocky scars appeared on tops of hills and pine trees and aspen grew in segregated thickets. Spots of grass, the lush shade of spring, and wildflowers grew wherever they found water. The air, as the sun fell closer to the horizon, cooled noticeably and let it be known that winter could come any minute on the summit of the Rockies.

After dinner Cal rode his mustang into the little mining town near the summit. I went for a walk and sat down in the sagebrush flat to stare at the Wind River range, snow-capped mountains. As I watched the sun went down and the last piece of ground that remained lit was the tips of the peaks.

I imagined that the sun was reflecting off the Pacific Ocean. After all we were on the backbone of the continent.

Just before complete darkness Yellow barked and Cal whistled in answer. He rode into camp and next to the fire he took from his coat two of the biggest, reddest apples I ever laid eyes on and threw them to Willie and me; then Cal handed one each to Mother and Pa. We were smiling and trying to eat our apples. South Pass apples — uncommonly sweet.

Our daily source of food was meat. Cal unlimbered his Hawken every time we saw a rabbit or antelope and no denying, Cal was a sure-shot.

Late one afternoon, two rabbits were cleaned, skinned and lying in the coolbox in the wagon. Cal and I were gunning for rabbit number three when Yellow, back at the wagon with Willie, started barking. She was disturbed, you could tell that from her voice.

"Better have a look-see," Cal said and we rode up toward the stationary wagon. Ahead on the skyline of the hill were four mounted Indians. Against the sun they were difficult to see but Cal moved forward, calling a greeting.

"They're Shoshone," he turned to us and said. Mother looked worried and Pa sat tight with a handful of reins. A conversation was carried on between Cal and the Indians; we couldn't make head nor tail of the discussion.

"They say this is their land and that we are trespassing. They want food in exchange for passage. Joe and Willie, go get those rabbits."

We fetched the rabbits from the back of the wagon and handed them to Cal. The Indians moved close. They were dressed in buckskin, looking gaunt and well-traveled. The Indian who did the talking wore a black reservation hat and one other had a feather in his hair. All wore belts and holsters and it appeared it would not take much to set them off, have them draw revolvers and kill us.

Cal made a ceremony of giving away our dinner, the two rabbits; as the Indians accepted, one of our hens let out an egg-laying squawk. The Indians looked at each other and the brave with the feather dismounted and circled to the back of the wagon. There was dust and commotion; he returned carrying two hens upside down by the feet. They were flapping their wings in a desperate attempt to get away. They could not.

Cal spoke with the Indians and finally turned toward Pa and said, "They will settle on the rabbits and two hens. That is the best we can do."

The Indians, each choosing meat or fowl for dinner, rode away in the same direction we were headed — west. And the hens, those poor unfortunate creatures, were making a gurgling sound like they had a lump in their throats. Mother cried.

We traveled late that night, a bright moon lit the rocks and low sage with soft white light. Up ahead on the road I saw feathers, black and gray from a Plymouth Rock laying hen. The Indians were getting ready for dinner.

The high plateau country west of South Pass was as Cal said it would be. We traveled for a number of miles along the bank of the Dry Sandy River. There were bright-colored agate stones polished by sand lying in the creekbed and in a few scattered holes brackish water stood, poison to the taste.

We camped near Juel Creek which was a trickle of water that disappeared into Dry Sandy. The grass that grew near this moisture was a welcome relief to the barren landscape. We slept well that night but come morning, as soon as I was on my feet, I knew something was wrong. Cal and Pa were standing near the fire, Cal drawing a map on the ground with the toe of his boot and Pa nodding his head every once in a while as he listened. I walked behind Cal, stood toe to the line drawn south.

"I cut off to California here. You folks go straight to Oregon. Joe, I guess this is goodbye. I've enjoyed your company. Remember, always be a man with backbone."

Cal extended his hand and I squeezed hard. I knew it would be the last time our skin would touch.

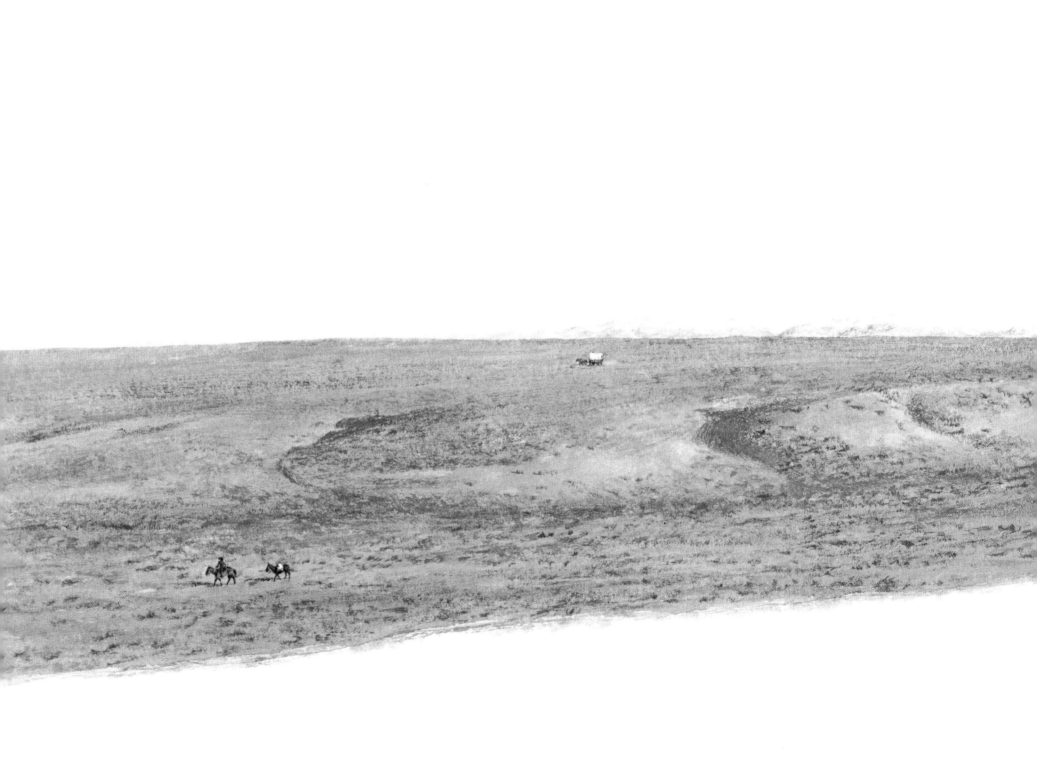

Cal accompanied us to the top of a short bluff overlooking our camp on Juel Creek. He split away then following the ridge around and recrossing the Dry Sandy while we started across a long flat. From that particular point in the middle of nowhere we diverged, two trails of dust going in different directions. Occasionally I could locate the tiny dots that were the mustang and pack mule; after awhile they disappeared.

I was six years old when we came west, rode a little white Shetland pony all the way. My uncle give him to me before we left Iowa.

Dad had a general rule that I had to stay close to the wagon. He would say, "George, you go riding away and somebody is going to knock you in the head and steal your horse." Usually I stayed beside the wagon, that way if there was trouble all Pa had to do was reach down and pick up his rifle. He always kept it loaded.

My horse was named Pet — named him that myself. He would eat carrots, when I had them, right out of my hand. Pet and me, we was like bread and butter.

The reason we started the trip was because a cousin had come out to Seattle and liked it real well. He wrote to Dad, said there was work and it didn't cost nothing to live. He claimed there were deer and antelope, ducks on the river and pheasants for the taking. Pa decided anything was better than Iowa and we fixed up the farm wagon, built a bed and put up bows and canvas to keep out the rain. I rode Pet, I wasn't about to be cooped up in some wagon.

We were prepared for a six-month trip, we carried a barrel of flour and Dad had plenty of ammunition. He shot our meat — we ate antelope, rabbits, birds and once he killed a buffalo. He could have killed more but a buffalo is so big and we didn't like to waste meat.

Dad's rifle was never out of arm's reach. At night he slept with it and was a damn lucky fact that he did. We took precautions every night before we went to sleep, like chaining and padlocking our horses to one of the wheels of the wagon.

We slept inside and this one night Dad woke up to a noise. It was a metal against metal grinding sound, the wagon wiggled ever so slightly. Dad lifted the back flap and peeked outside. The night was fairly bright, stars and the moon was shining. Out through the sagebrush our horses moved and someone was leading them. Dad yelled and it woke us all. I looked at him silhouetted against the sky. His gun went to his shoulder and he fired.

''You renegades, get the hell out of here,'' Dad yelled. If he had wanted to kill whoever was stealing our horses he could have. Pa was a very good shot.

Two men were responsible, they had come to our camp, jacked up the wagon and blocked it. We had no warning until the wheel squeaked when they took it off. They had the wheel and the horses, going for the hills when Dad shot over their heads. The wheel was dropped right there and they ran to a thicket of brush.

We never knew who they was but suspected Indians, though they could have been white men. White men who lived out there in the middle of nowhere was no better than Indians, maybe worse.

All the Pfannebecker children — two brothers, two sisters and I — were born in Iowa but Dad had it pretty tough trying to farm and we moved on to Buffalo, Missouri. Missouri wasn't any better, there were crop failures and we starved out. Dad loaded us in two wagons and we headed west without a cent to our name.

Dad figured on working some along the way and in Kansas we stopped while he got a job in harvest. We camped there and a few other emigrants camped with us. Their men were in need of work, too. After a couple weeks Dad wanted to get traveling and he called for his pay. There was no problem about it, the farmer paid what he owed. Dad hid the money somewhere in the wagon. None of us, including Mother, knew where it was. Dad was the only one, yet sometime between when he hid it and came back to check, the money was stolen. Nobody said anything about it but one family pulled out right away. Dad believed they took our money.

We existed on jackrabbits and sage hens. The menu never varied. Coming across Wyoming somewhere the boys shot two sage hens and were sitting in camp picking and cleaning them when a big black dog wandered in and came toward the boys. He growled, showed teeth and in every way appeared ferocious. The boys threw him the feathers and entrails because they were afraid not to. The big dog left camp complaining about the amount of food he had gotten but Ed and Harry weren't about to give away our meal. Next morning Dad was visiting with a farmer who lived in the neighborhood.

"We had a big black dog come into camp last night," Dad told him. "He acted real mean. Do you know to whom he belongs?"

"Did he have kind of a star on his forehead and long, matted hair?" asked the farmer.

"Yes, he did."

"Boy oh boy," said the farmer, "that wasn't a dog. That was a wolf and if what you gave him hadn't suited him, you wouldn't be here now. That devil wolf."

We left Battle Creek, Nebraska, hoping to reach Oregon before we ran out of money but it didn't work out that way.

Coming through Wyoming we turned north off the trail, Dad looking for work. In our family there was Father, Mother, and my older brother Arthur. I was three years old. Traveling with us were the Whitcombs, the old man about 70 and his sons George and Elmer, both grown men.

Up along the Yellowstone was the first time we ran into Indians and when they came riding up to our wagons old man Whitcomb crawled in back under the quilts and hid. He was deathly afraid that they were going to scalp him.

When we went to set up evening camp the Indians returned and Mother gave them food to eat. The old man refused to come out of the wagon but we didn't let him spoil the fun.

We sat around the campfire and Dad made small talk with the chief. Wearing doeskin garments and a headdress made from eagle feathers, the chief must have been a very important fellow.

One of the chief's papooses was handed to him and he turned toward Dad and gave him away. Dad stood there in front of the fire and held the little boy in the air, over his head. The chief reached to where I was sitting and lifted me onto his lap. He smiled.

''Maybe we trade papooses,'' Dad said, making a little joke. But the chief didn't take it as a joke — not in the slightest.

''We trade,'' he said and held me in his powerful arms.

That scared Mother right now and she came over and took me away. Dad gave the chief back his papoose. The Indians were not pleased and they left camp abruptly.

We were scared for the next day or two, until we got off the reservation. Later we ran into some settlers and they told us we had been lucky. They said the last white folks who tried to cross the reservation never came out.

Of the four wagons that left Goodland, Kansas, only three made it clear through. Friends of our family who started the trip with us fell in love with a little valley we passed and decided to stay there. That was the last we heard from them.

The rest of us cut off the trail at Snake River and proceeded straight west but we ran into eastern Oregon Indian trouble. The Indians didn't come riding in shooting and attacking like you hear about. They snuck into camp in the middle of the night and stole all the horses.

We had a pair of mules on our wagon and the Indians didn't bother taking them. Still, there we were, three wagons and one team of mules, out in the middle of nowhere.

Father and one of his brothers went in pursuit riding the mules bareback, looking for the horses. A couple of ridges over they located the Indians. The Indians refused to give us back our animals for nothing but they did offer to trade for some of our loose cattle. The Lawrences weren't fond of killing so Father agreed. After all, horses were the most important.

Not Among the Living

Losing the company of Cal was like having an arm severed, it took a while to get used to the fact. But by the time we hit Green River I was so dehydrated and tired I could no longer spare the energy to think about Cal. He occupied a recess in my brain.

In the morning I was still exhausted from the long march without water. My body ached from head to toe but I pitched in and did my share, almost as much as Pa.

''Good job,'' Pa said as he came from behind to pat me on the shoulder. I was currying the team and combing stickers from their manes and tails. I rubbed my hands over their dirty white hides, pulled taut over rib cages.

For several days we camped near beaver workings on the bank of Green River and allowed our animals to rest.

We all enjoyed the reprieve and the one who enjoyed it most was Yellow. She went off by herself exploring raccoon tracks on the muddy bank and climbing as far as she could up fragmenting sandstone cliffs.

Willie was in a rundown condition and did not join Yellow on her sorties; for the first time in her life Willie's dog played and hunted on her own. She enjoyed herself and each expedition became more extended in distance and length of time. In among the willows Yellow hunted; she chased jackrabbits until she either caught or lost them. Where she found the energy I do not know.

After dinner the last night at Green River we sat around the campfire listening to Yellow bark off in the distance. I lay there straining my ears and letting imagination follow the string of yips and barking beyond the edge of night: the chase, a deer on the run spinning through willow thickets, sliding downhill; or an antelope ahead running flat-out in the open.

"Willie," Mother said, speaking sharper than she needed, "you have gone completely through the bottoms of your boots. Only uppers aren't doing any good except to add weight. Tomorrow when we leave, you leave them here, okay?"

"Yes," Willie replied.

Willie was up first thing in the morning. I felt him crawl from under the blanket and heard him calling at the top of his lungs, "Yellow, Yellow, Yellow!"

"Where's Yellow?" I asked, getting up and pulling on my boots.

"I wish I knew," he said and went on calling, going in ever widening circles from the wagon. As I did chores his voice became the sound of a fly slowly circling. Willie was not back in time for breakfast and it was not until Pa and I were hitching the team of mules that he came into camp.

"Pa, Pa, can we wait for a little bit? I've looked everywhere. If we just wait I know Yellow will be back. I promise."

"I don't know what all of a sudden got into her," Pa said, "but I guess this once we can wait. But only until noon. After this you better tie her up at night."

The sun stood straight over our heads and the mules were impatient to hit the road. Pa started them across the Green River ford with a double-roll of his tongue off the roof of his mouth, "Click-click."

Willie trailed along, barefooted, calling over his shoulder and whistling with two fingers in his mouth. For the first few miles he could have seen Yellow attempting to catch us but we turned away from the river into a blind canyon. At dinner stop I let Willie take Blaze so he could go look for Yellow.

"Thanks, Joe, thanks a lot. I won't forget this," he said and rode back the way we had come.

I heard Blaze nicker from off in the distance and the mules answer. I turned around and looked, fully expecting to see Yellow trotting alongside; she wasn't. Willie was crushed.

That night Willie said to me, "Think I'll ever see Yellow again?" And I answered, "Sure, sure you will, Yellow is probably on our trail right now," but in my mind I was lying. I was old enough to know about such things, or at least to have a feeling about them.

My reassurance did little, if anything for Willie. He was like a boy split down the middle and in the morning when we left, half of him went west and the other half east searching for his dog.

Dinner came and Willie dabbed at his stew, moved it from one side of the bowl to the other. He said he couldn't eat and later that night he told me, "I know what happened. It was a pack of wolves."

A week went by and we were coming up Bear River valley when a freighter overtook and passed us.

"Hey, Mister," Willie hollered when the freighter was right alongside. "Did you happen to see a yellow dog down the road somewhere? She would be headed in this direction."

Freighters don't pull up on command of little boys, they rarely ever speak to one another, but this freighter noticed a masked urgency in the request.

"Yeh, Sonny, I seen a dog," drawled the freighter, "but it was way back on Green River. She was a yellar color and the scrawniest bitch I've laid eyes on. Weren't no meat, just hide and bone. I tried to get close but she growled, showed teeth. I didn't want to get bit so I left her alone. Strange part was, she was guardin' an old pair of boots. Hell, wasn't nothing left but uppers."

After that Willie acted as if he had been beat with a stick and the country we passed through did nothing to relieve his frame of mind. It was drier than a preacher's sermon and I knew that if we stopped for long the wagon would sink in the sand. Scrubby sagebrush was everywhere.

Most of the time Willie and I walked side by side, me leading Blaze. The few times I tried to ride my weight would make Blaze unsure on his feet, he stumbled, could not walk a straight line. His strength was failing and if we did not get to grass pretty soon there was going to be a dead horse on our hands.

We passed the skeletons of animals, they were mostly cows but occasionally there would be horse skulls. Never before had I considered how cruel to man and beast the desert can be. It allows no mistakes.

We followed the bottom of the broad valley. There was no grass to speak of and only stunted sage broke the flatness. On the sides of the hills, quite some distance away, were juniper trees. My God, they looked good and as I walked I thought about lying in the shade of a juniper, going to sleep.

Into the world of the desert flowed a river, the Snake. Never in my life was I so happy to see water. The deep green color of the Snake River in such bleak surroundings of sand and sage — nothing could have looked better.

The reprieve from the desert did not last. For a few days we followed the Snake, Blaze and the mules gorging themselves on the grass at water's edge, then the river veered away to the north as we continued due west. This happened several times but we always, eventually, returned to the Snake and when we did we would lay over and Mother would wash clothes and bake.

When we had to cross Snake River we had the option of Three Island Ford or paying to be transported by ferry. We were warned at Glenns Ferry that taking a wagon across Three Island Ford, into the swift current, was dangerous and Pa decided we would take the ferry.

I had figured we would camp near the river since it was going to be a week before we came back to it but Pa said we would keep moving. He was in a hurry now to reach Oregon.

Boise was a long time coming and when we pulled in we found a fairly good-sized town. We paused long enough to buy supplies and then were back on the desert.

After crossing the Snake River on a cable ferry, we landed and Pa announced in his husky voice, ''We're in Oregon. By God, we made it!''

Oregon. That came as such a shock. Pa had said it was green year around in Oregon — but here we were in the same desert we had been in for weeks, not even a weed would grow here. Oregon, my foot!

''Things will get better,'' Pa promised at dinner. It had to — we were making dry camp, couldn't wash and I had only enough water to make my throat thirsty.

The following day was hot as usual, we topped a long rise and down below in the valley ran the Malheur River. The water was low and muddy but we were thirsty by that time and we rushed into the shallow stream and lay down. We were like hogs at a wallow. Mother stayed ankle deep dabbing at her neck and forehead with a handkerchief she dipped in and out of the strong coffee-colored water.

There was a long thirty-mile stretch between the Malheur and our final return to the Snake. Nothing grew and few animals lived among the stunted sagebrush in the back country. The sun went down as a full moon rose on our right and we continued to travel. Pa planned to water and camp at Tub Springs but we never found a spring and the lateness of the hour dictated dry camp.

I awoke in the middle of the night; coyotes in a small circle around us were yipping and howling. And as I looked, in that dizzy state between sleep and awake, I saw a slice of moon missing. There was a lunar eclipse. The light from the moon became dimmer until the country was dark and at the instant the light disappeared the coyotes stopped howling. It was as if they had been praying for a piece of the moon and their request was denied. Even as night became brighter and the moon began to reappear the coyotes remained silent. Then the sun arrived, the pack let out a single chorus and we started another day on the trail.

The Snake River bent east from the road as we entered the confines of Burnt River canyon. The sides of the canyon went straight up, straight down. All I could see of the day was a little wedge of blue overhead. The bottom was strewn with boulders and rock, rock, rock. Mother complained that the jolting gave her toothaches.

The canyon was smoking hot, rocks radiated heat and rattlesnakes curled in the shade. And one day when I felt I could stand the confinement no longer the canyon opened to a high valley. I stretched my arms and Blaze galloped toward the willow-banked river.

Travel was on the valley floor but it was soon evident from the grade and by looking back, we were climbing. The cool mornings and evenings in this high mountain pass made a coat a necessity. And then we broke over the top. Below was a flat tabletop land that ran in the direction of a distant range of mountains. Heavy clouds blocked the sun but as we watched the clouds lifted and exposed peaks of white. Snow had fallen in the mountains.

Powder River valley opened to us like a book. The bottom was marshy and home to ducks and Canadian geese. From long stretches of cattails rose the rim of the valley and in all directions, a circle, there were mountain ranges. Snow topped mountain peaks and below timberline the dark green of the forest was interrupted by gold splotches of tamarack.

Our road stayed to the upper side of the valley floor and except for wet spots and mosquitoes the going was good. It changed to bad at the mouth of a canyon where the trail dropped fifteen hundred feet in a mile and bottomed on the floor of another similar valley. Undoubtedly that descent was the worst grade on the Oregon Trail. We came down without mishap in a chilling rain. The wet made the shale rock all the more dangerous and testimony to failure was littered down the hill: pieces of wagons, crushed packboxes and even piano keys.

Taking a passerby's word we turned east off the Oregon Trail to search for hot springs. If they were all the man said, we would be able to hard boil eggs, wash and not have to heat a drop of water.

The hot spring made a cloud that invaded the coldness of the afternoon and as we entered the curtain of fog we saw others camped; out in the center sat a hollowed log bathtub. Children were lined taking turns. Mothers scrubbed them behind the ears and as soon as clean clothes were put on, the children laughed again, playing with a yellow dog. She barked at us, a friendly bark.

Willie awoke from his daydream. "Yellow, Yellow," he cried. He jumped from the wagon and started running. In mid-stride Willie became aware of his mistake. The dog was not Yellow and the truth of that doubled Willie over. It was as if he had had the wind knocked out of him.

Willie was heartbroken; he went away to be alone. While he was gone Mother visited with the other women and learned the dog was a bitch with pups ready to wean. Did we want one, a woman asked. "Oh, heavens, yes," Mother said and when Willie returned she told him the news. His eyes jumped wide-open. He was happy, and when it came to choosing Willie picked from the litter a replica of his only other dog, Yellow. Choosing a pup was like Willie giving in to the fact that Yellow was gone. But my brother was happier than he had been in weeks. The dog was good for him.

That night at the fire Willie said, "I'm going to call her Two. Just the number Two."

Two was spoiled with petting as Willie tried to take over the role of mother. The bitch came by several times to make sure her pup was in good hands. When she did Willie would rub her behind the ears and show her Two.

The pup slept with us that night and in the morning we were away in a driving storm of rain and sleet. Oh, it was miserable and my breath came as smoke. Inside the wagon, on the bed, Willie played with Two as we made our way across the valley floor toward the town of La Grande. We planned to lay over but when we got there the smithy told Pa that if we expected to beat winter over the mountains we had no time to lose.

From La Grande the grade into the Blue Mountains was steep. Mother and Willie had to walk and Willie carried the pup. On top grew a forest of pine trees, the first good stand of timber I saw. We stayed at the edge of a clearing and followed the bench around until we had to return to the river. This was accomplished with an abrupt descent.

With recent rains the river was muddy and swollen. Pa checked the ford and started the wagon forward into the swirling current.

I couldn't say for sure what happened next, whether the wheel hit a rock or what, but Two fell from Willie's grasp and into the river torrent. Willie was right behind. By the time I could react Willie had Two by the scruff of the neck and was heading for shore.

We immediately started a fire and I ran to get fuel. Mother wrapped Willie and Two in a quilt and sat them in front of the fire. Two dried quickly and was ready to resume play but Willie continued to sit by the fire. He just couldn't warm up.

Next morning the cold and fog of the day seemed to have settled in Willie's bones. His small body was racked with chill spasms. Mother heated rocks in the fire and put them in bed but no amount of heat warmed Willie; his feet were bricks in an icehouse.

Pa came over by the fire to where Mother was standing. He took her hands in his and quietly told her that the weather was changing for the worse; we would be lucky if we didn't hit snow. We had to go on even though it might not be best for Willie. Four lives were at stake. Mother agreed.

We made Willie as comfortable as possible in the wagon. Moving made him uncomfortable and from near the wagon where I was riding I could hear Willie moan in his sleep. And then the snow started falling. Huge flakes drifted down, clung to the arms of pine trees and piled on the ground. The thought of coming this far for nothing haunted me.

Over the summit and the snow tapered off, dusted distant ridges and left the lower valleys bare. We made camp at Emigrant Springs. The air still threatened snow and after staking Blaze I went to check on Willie. I lifted the flap; Willie lay with his eyes open, he winced at the light. I spoke but he did not answer and then he finally mumbled something. All I caught was, "Take care of Two."

I called Mother. She bundled the quilts tighter around Willie. The look I had seen in my brother's eye the moment the light hit, that empty look; I knew and had to get away.

I ran and then ran some more. Eventually on a pinnacle of land at the top of the mountain I stopped. On either side, a thousand feet below, the bottoms of two canyons came together.

I sat on a slab of rimrock facing west and beside me growing from a crack in the rock was a gnarled pine. The dwarf might have been a hundred years old, it grew in size according to its confines. There was a trace of snow where I was but below on the bald canyon walls dried grass was blowing in the breeze.

Far to the west, two hundred miles, the jagged peaks of the Cascades became visible. The Willamette was just on the other side of that range. And the sky that was colored gold and yellow changed to a melting red. The Cascades stood in black outline as I turned toward camp. It got dark on me, I stumbled over snow-covered rocks and wind-blown snags. And then I was in camp beside the fire drinking a cup of hot broth.

Mother went to feed Willie and from that direction there came such a wail — no words could describe her wail and the hairs jumped on the nape of my neck. I shivered.

"Oh God, oh God, oh God," mother repeated and Pa was at her side. She cried into his shoulder.

"Stay back, Joe," Pa said, turning toward me. "Your brother is dead."

Mother sat on a log staring hard into the fire. She dabbed at her eyes and Pa got up, took a quilt off Willie and wrapped Mother's shoulders with it. She thanked him with a look and Pa walked away. He took a shovel, threw it on his shoulder and picked up the lantern. As he walked away the lantern pushed the night from around him.

After he returned and washed the mud and dirt from his hands, Pa, Mother and I slept in one bed by the fire. We hugged all through the night and the wind whistled in the pines.

Darkness went on forever until the eastern sky slowly showed blue, gray and then emerald green. I noticed the subtle change in color and wondered if I was seeing now for Willie.

The sun was over the horizon before Mother stepped into the wagon. She wrapped Willie in a bright red wool blanket. When she was done Pa lifted Willie into his arms and started walking. I followed behind Mother, carrying the shovel like I had seen Pa do the night before.

Using our driving reins Pa and I lowered Willie into the hole Pa had dug. Pa pulled the reins to his side, stood and said, "Lord, I don't know what your reasons are for taking our boy," he stopped and bit his lower lip. "Lord, now that you got him, take care of him."

Mother poured the first handful of dirt and went to a pole thicket and cried. Pa and I stayed. The first few shovels, on top of the red blanket, were the hardest.

Along toward spring Daddy took a notion to move to Oregon. He said we were going — Mom got the children ready. At that time there was two girls, Carrie and one-year-old Bessie; I was in my mom waiting to be born.

In our neighborhood, Mercer County, Missouri, there was an old Cherokee squaw who midwifed. Daddy talked her into bringing a wagon and following. Another family with a pregnant woman decided to come along; the other woman was due the same time as Mother.

Before we left Mother prepared a baby box into which she packed everything. She had rags and baby clothes, diapers and small quilts. When done she stowed the box in an out-of-the-way place.

The day our family left there was Daddy, Mom, Carrie and Bessie all in one wagon. The second wagon belonged to the old Indian and her husband and the third wagon contained the other expecting couple as well as a friend they knew.

This friend was a hillbilly and a most disgusting individual. He was filthy as mortal sin. The only excuse this creature had for looking and acting as he did was the fact he didn't know how he was supposed to be around folks.

Mother saw him eat eggs by crushing the shell with one hand and gulping down white, yolk and all. What he missed drained down the sides of his mouth and mixed with trail dirt.

Whatever he ate was, so to speak, on the hoof. Mother once saw him catch little chickens — he twisted their heads off, stripped feathers and heated what was left, feet and all, over a flame. One pass on one side and a pass on the other. He tore off portions of the chicken, starting with the legs, and shoved these inside his horrible mouth, pulling clean with his teeth. Blood dripped from his chin and when he was through he wiped with the cuff of his long-sleeved shirt.

The manners exhibited were loathsome. Mother took sick to her stomach — she couldn't stand to lay eyes on the man. She quit eating dinner.

When little Bessie came down with fever, chills and difficulty breathing Mother blamed the filthy habits of the hillbilly. And the sicker Bessie became the more Mother thought back to the time she first went west, as a child. On that trip Mother looked on as her own mother took sick, then died. They wrapped Grandmother in a sheet, buried her alongside the trail. Mother watched the men shovel in the grave, pile rocks on top and then Grandfather took out a Bible, read from it while the wind kept turning the pages.

Mother nursed Bessie; she put wet rags on her head when Bessie was hot and quilts when she grew cold, but it was like Bessie had turned and walked toward the horizon. She kept going until life walked out of her body.

On a green grassy hill they buried Bessie. Daddy took things out of the grub box; used that for a coffin. He dug a hole right at the top of the hill so that little Bessie could see in all directions.

I was born a few days after Bessie died and Mother said she was so run-down she and I would surely have died had it not been for the midwife squaw. She pulled us through and because of that Mother named me Lizzie after her.

By the time we landed in La Grande, Oregon, quite a noticeable birthmark had appeared on my face. It started as a very dark spot on one cheek and spread from there. Mother said the reason was due to the filthy man who had made the crossing with them; her nausea, she said.

Quite a few years passed and a friend of the folks, Jeff Bull, came by and said he was planning a trip from La Grande back east to Missouri. He had heard Daddy tell of burying Bessie and said he would be on the lookout.

In Iowa Jeff Bull found the grassy hill and later he told us: ''They started a town at the base of the hill. As far as the hill goes there can be no doubt — it was green and covered with wild flowers like no other hill around. And on top was a graveyard. A pole fence surrounded the spot and right in the middle was a grave and a marker which read, 'Emigrant Baby, Unknown.'

''I knew who it was — your girl Bessie — so I told them so in town.

''When I returned a storm was moving in across Iowa. Rain and lightning were striking everywhere but I swung back on the grassy knoll. One last look.

''There was the most lovely tombstone you will ever see in your life. It read, 'Emigrant Baby, Bessie Page'.''

I was named after Savannah, Georgia, by my father. He had been there after the Civil War and I guess he liked the place. The war took a lot out of our family — Dad fought on the side of the South, Mother's father was killed by Yankees. She was but a little girl at the time and was looking for her father when a company of Yankee soldiers found her. One told her that if she was looking for her father she would find him in the tree patch. When she went, she found him — hanging.

My father, Martin Van Buren Smith, got a small pension from fighting in that war. For quite a few years he saved it; then one day he bought supplies and told us we were going to Oregon. When we pulled out of Seneca, Missouri, we had our old wagon, a team

Father bought special, and our regular team — Barney and Coley. Barney was a sorry excuse for a horse. He had asthma and was spring-footed; once he stepped on me and broke my ankle but I knew he didn't mean it.

Mother cooked over a campfire and at night I slept in the wagon with the folks. My six brothers slept in a tent. During the day we walked. Sure, if we got tired we could catch up to the wagon and ride, but when we were rested we had to get back out.

One time my brother just younger than me, William Henry, was climbing from the wagon and slipped. I was witness but it happened so fast — there wasn't anything I could do. He fell to the ground and the back wheel of the wagon ran over his chest. I thought he was dead — I was sure of it. Lucky for him, though, it was in soft sand. The weight pushed him down until he was half-buried but it never broke a bone.

Barney and Coley kept up with the other team pretty good but the farther we went the worse Barney became — though he did pick up a bit in Idaho when he got to fruit. He and I both loved Idaho. I was an apple fiend and Barney went for pears.

Then Barney's asthma got bad, he could only take a few steps before he would have a seizure, stop and go to wheezing. Dad unhitched Barney and brought up a mare that had a colt on her.

We left Barney where he stopped pulling. I looked back — he tried to follow but another attack hit. That was the last I saw of Barney.

A few weeks after we left Monte Vista, Colorado, I stopped a horseshoe with my face. Broke my jaw there and here. The horse's name was Florence. Florence was tied to a tree and you know how a ten-year-old boy is — I wasn't watching where I was going.

I came in with an armload of wood for the fire, walked behind Florence and I guess she thought I was the dog or something. She let me have it — both barrels. Knocked me over backwards down a bank and into the river. Now I don't remember none of this except what was told to me but apparently Dad saw what happened and if he hadn't jumped in the river I would have drowned.

I was unconscious. I don't remember being kicked but Florence made a bulls-eye and by the time Dad fished me out of the river my face started to swell and get the fever.

We didn't let my injury slow things down. I was kept in the back of the wagon while we traveled. One afternoon we set camp, 75 miles from the nearest town, and Dad put me on a blanket in the shade beneath the wagon.

An old buck Indian came riding in on a cayuse while Mother was cooking dinner. The Indian got off his horse and led it beside of the wagon. He sticks his head under, looks at me with the rag tied around my head holding my jaw together. Then he got back on his cayuse and rode away. Never said one damn word.

Down where we were camped there was a point of small timber and brush. Up on top was a bench, the desert started there. The buck rode off in that direction and after a while a squaw came off the bench. She crawled under the wagon and took a look at me, got up and found our ax. She chopped a branch off a tree and hiked up on top of the bench. When she came back she was carrying a whole stick full of those flat leaf cactus. She held them over the campfire and burned the briars off. When the job was done she made motions toward Mother. The squaw didn't talk anything but Indian, but she got Mother to understand she needed rags. Mother tore a bedsheet.

The squaw took a piece of the cloth, wrapped it around the cactus and started pounding it with the flat side of the ax. When the cactus turned to pulp she came over and tied it around my jaw. The squaw left.

About a week's time had gone by since Florence had kicked me, and I had never come out of it. But about two hours after the squaw put the poultice on, I opened my eyes. I couldn't move my head but Mother saw my eyes come open and she ran over and asked, "George, George, are you all right?" 'Course I couldn't answer her, all I could do was mumble.

That cactus had done so much good that Dad didn't want to run out; he gathered a grain sack about half full and tied it to one of the wagon bows. Until we got into Park City that is all Mom used. To me it was an ice pack, it was so cool. The heartbeat I felt in my fevered face finally quit and by then the swelling in my jaw had gone down.

Park City was a little mining town and they had a doctor there. Dad fetched him to look at me. He took one look and said, "The best I can tell the jaw is set straight. I can't do a thing."

Mother explained about the squaw's medicine and the doctor said, "Well, he's improving. I would say go ahead and use the cactus."

And that was all the medicine I ever took.

Landing

The heart had gone from traveling, we left it behind in Willie's grave.

From the summit of the Blue Mountains the west side descends stairstep fashion along knife-edged points of land. Deep bald canyons cut on either side. I felt insulated from these surroundings. I only recall the mules running downhill as fast as they could, trying to stay ahead of the wagon. And as we passed Pendleton there was a cowboy breaking a cayuse on main street. Traffic was stopped to watch until the animal broke, trembled like a wet dog and the cowboy slid off its back.

West of Pendleton the wind blew continually. I tried to pick up the smell of the Pacific Ocean on the breeze but only dry sagebrush air burned my nostrils and I became tired of leaning into the wind, eyes closed to keep out sand. There was no water. We made do and were miserable.

Rock, sage and alkali flats were our entire existence. And then just before John Day canyon we topped out, could see in all directions and like a wall to the west the snow-capped peaks of the Cascades formed a barrier.

Past John Day canyon the land leveled for quite some distance before breaking into rolling hills and then ravines. Pa said we were near the Columbia and we turned north following above a canyon.

And there it was; the Columbia, the mighty Columbia. I had heard so many stories about the great river, had looked forward to it so much that sighting the water revived my spirit. I felt better inside and the blue water of the Columbia flowed away through the gorge it had cut in the Cascades.

A short five miles after hitting the Columbia we crossed the Deschutes and climbed above the river, one day out from The Dalles.

In The Dalles we camped on a vacant lot for several days before Pa arranged space for us on a ferry. Camped there with dogs barking and people stirring was not our usual style. But the enthusiasm, the hustle and bustle of everyone was infectious. Mother put on a dress for the first time in months and went shopping.

As we arrived at the ferry early in the morning everyone was excited. Small groups stood on the deck, each person trying to out-talk all others. A farmer brought a load of hogs on board and they commenced squealing.

We made our way downriver and I forgot about all else. I stood at the bow staring at the sheer rock walls of the gorge, the misty waterfalls that fell a thousand feet to the Columbia. It was an awesome sight.

Portland. We stayed in a hotel; the mules and Blaze boarded at a livery. Next morning the wagon rumbled over cobblestone streets and people we passed turned to stare. I caught our reflection in a store window. God, we looked trail weary; clothes patched over patch and our skin dry and gaunt. As we continued down the valley past farms we were invited in to eat and once were given a basket of fruit.

I had in my mind's eye what Uncle Elmo's farm looked like, dreaming of eternal spring, cows grazing and fat hogs. I had visions that when we pulled in a hen would cackle to say she had laid her daily egg. But what I had envisioned was nowhere near accurate.

The dense jungle foliage of the Willamette Valley drops leaves before winter but a few lingering yellow leaves hung from maple trees and viney thickets hugged both sides of the road. Vast forests of fir covered the distant hills and fingers came down on the valley floor. The firs stood tall and mighty except in areas being cleared where there were blackened stumps. And rain. The rain came steady.

We were soaked to the skin but excited as we turned down Uncle Elmo's lane. The kids were the first to see us; they ran forward, shouting at the top of their lungs to their Ma and Pa.

They were living in a small log cabin and were working on clearing land. There was no fat livestock, only dogs and kids and as we climbed to the ground Aunty swept through the door, gathered us in an embrace and kissed each individually. Uncle Elmo shook hands all the way around.

The children were jumping up and down playing with Two, we were smiling, laughing, having a good time and then Uncle Elmo asked, "Where in the dickens is little Willie?"

For some strange reason I thought arriving at Uncle Elmo's meant the end of the trip. It did not and we camped next to their log cabin while Pa discovered land prices in the area were above our means. It was suggested we look elsewhere.

Pa was disillusioned by the prospects and wanted to take a job in the woods but Mother insisted he find a farm. She told him, "Jackson, we can do it. If it means clearing ground we can. Somewhere there has got to be a farm for us."

The overwhelming desire to have a place of our own led Pa to take a pig in the poke. He bought a quarter section of land sight unseen. The location of our new place was a few miles east of the town of Grand Ronde, in the northwest part of the Willamette Valley. That, plus the name of the previous owner, was all we knew.

Grand Ronde is nestled against the coastal mountain range and as we pulled into town a fog hung low and a light misty rain fell. At the general merchandise store we went in and Pa asked, "How do we find the old Robinson place?"

"Old Robinson place — uh — go past the Agency, turn left up the lane, can't miss 'er, only house up there."

"Agency?" I asked. "What kind of agency?"

"Indian agency — and something between you and me. Don't leave nothin' lying around. It'll grow legs and walk off."

I was reluctant — Indians — especially since those words shouted as we left Kansas came back to me: "Watch out for Indians." Now we were going to be next door neighbors.

We turned down the lane and in the distance the deserted barn and house appeared. Fog hugged tightly to the hills behind. As we came closer and the dilapidated state of the farm became evident I wondered why we had come west. We left better in Kansas.

Don Gray

Catching and clawing blackberry vines grew everywhere and I battled them along the house getting to a broken window. I crawled inside and in the few seconds it took for me to open the door I looked around. The ceiling was leaking and the wallpaper was rerolling. The rooms were bare except for a fireplace and an armload of wood on the hearth. That small gesture by the last resident helped improve my frame of mind. I opened the door, invited Pa and Mother inside and started a fire.

After feeding Blaze and the mules leftover hay from the barn we had our dinner and that night instead of sleeping on the hard wood floor the three of us slept in the haymow and dreamed about how we would make the farm our home.

The next morning Mother began cleaning house. Pa and I worked shoveling manure from the barn and then we unloaded the wagon. Willie's things we put in the grub box and set away in one corner of the barn. If he ever returned his things would be together.

While we were working Two played by running between the house and barn, watching progress. She stopped to bark and kept at it until Pa sent me to see what was the trouble. I looked up the road in the direction Two was barking and saw a hearse — a big, black hearse — parked on our lane. And an Indian buck in a silk hat sat straight as could be in the driver's seat.

When the Indian saw I had control of Two he drove in and I could see at the windows of his hearse, with the curtains pulled back, round little Indian faces pressed against the glass.

"Call me Winchester Jim," the Indian said. He pounded the butt end of his Winchester rifle against the top of the hearse and a squaw and a tribe of little Indians jumped to the ground.

The buck, hair in braids and wearing a flannel shirt, sat on the seat until Pa appeared. Then he stepped down and shook Pa's hand. He repeated his name, "Winchester Jim."

Mother was in the kitchen when the hearse pulled into our yard. What caught her attention were the sounds of playing children. She came to the front porch with a loaf of fresh bread and butter on a cutting board. She gave each child a slice and when Winchester Jim made a motion of rubbing his belly Mother made a special effort to bring him and his squaw a slice.

After that Winchester Jim and his family would occasionally appear on our front porch. They stood single file, with Winchester Jim in back, until Mother presented each with a treat. Winchester Jim always paid his way. One time he brought a hindquarter of deer, another time beaded moccasins for Mother. We were always glad to see Winchester Jim.

One morning Pa and I packed a maul, wedges, an ax and a cross-cut saw up the hill behind our house. We figured to cut a load of fence posts by dinner. Two came with us.

While we were gone Mother went about her chores as usual. She fed the chickens but they seemed bothered. Mother looked for a skunk or a raccoon but could find nothing and left the chickens squawking at their own shadows.

In the barn the mules were blowing air and kicking at the sides of their stalls. Mother stepped around the end of the barn — at that instant a mountain lion broke from shadow into sunlight.

Mother froze, she was a statue with a pail of eggs in hand. She tried to scream, could not. Tried to run, could not. She was stuck in her tracks and the mountain lion knew it. He took small mincing steps, slow motion, first one foot and then another. He moved without a sound, a slight eddy of wind rustled leaves on the ground.

Between barn and house the sound of a shot echoed and re-echoed. Long minutes passed before Mother opened her eyes and saw the cat stretched flat and bleeding. She looked down the lane and there was Winchester Jim sitting on the high driver's seat of his hearse. He waved his rifle in salute.

After brother George had his jaw broken by the horse we moved slow. Mother fixed him a bed near the fire every night and I don't know how many days went by that we expected him to die. The world was big and lonely.

It was the Indian squaw with the prickly pear cactus who saved George's life. God bless Indians! George began drinking liquids through a hollow grass straw. He improved day by day and when we finally did get to a doctor he could do no more than the squaw.

At one of our roadside camps a man rode in and said he owned a farm nearby — he said he could use a man for a few days. Pay would be a place to camp, pasture for the horses, plenty of milk, some eggs and such vegetables as they had. Dad took the job; we welcomed the stop.

George got his first real nourishment here; the farmer's wife fixed up a concoction of milk and egg, sugar and nutmeg. She made George drink.

The farm family had children who approximated us in age. There were several hundred acres to the farm and it seemed to be overrun with ground squirrels. The children had a job of killing the ground squirrels and for every five tails they brought in their father paid them one cent. They asked if we would like in on the deal. We were all for it.

Kids have to resort to pretty devious methods in order to catch a ground squirrel. The way we did it was to put a loop over their hole and pull it tight when they came out. After that we beat them to death with sticks.

We collected maybe a couple of dozen tails and turned them over to the other children. When they found out we killed the squirrels they were upset.

"Why did you go and do that?" they asked. "We just take the tails and turn them loose so they can grow another."

We were back on the road again and by now George was able to sit. I would have been perfectly happy to have stayed forever on the farm but the wandering blood in Dad made us move on. His Oregon fever was running hot.

For me the trip had lost its glamour, I was tired and ready to quit and then one sundown I saw an omen. The sky turned just as red a red as you can imagine. I had heard about the end of the world, when it is consumed by fire, and I thought the time had come. Next morning the world was still in place and we went on.

We made dry camp after dry camp, although never two in a row, and then late one afternoon we topped a little rise and there ahead was, of all things, a lake. Even the dead-tired horses broke into a trot but as we got near the shore we could see that the area was covered with bones of dead creatures.

It was a stark warning we did not take, never having heard about alkali. We unhitched the horses and they plunged in, drank so greedily we had to pull them back and let them drink again a while later.

We all waded into the water and drank. There was a funny, quite strong taste and below the surface the lake was loaded with wiggling water dogs. We were careful when we went to fill the water barrel that we did not include any. That night, though we were all sick from alkali, we did not dump the barrel. We could not predict when or where we might find water again.

Snake River was a blessing to us. The area was settled and at camp one evening a farmer came and asked if we would work. Dad put up his hay while Mother and us older children picked prunes. After the prunes were in Mother asked if we could have the summer apples that were going to waste. The farmer said sure, so for the next month we picked and dried apples. We filled seven flour sacks and were back on the road again.

Where we had stopped had been ideal in every respect and I was a bit put out that we had to keep moving. A month later, when we finally did reach our destination, I was actually a little mad. We had passed up a lot of country that looked more inviting than did Elgin, Oregon. On the other hand, I thought, there had been some terrible places we had gone through and Elgin looked good in comparison.

By the time we reached Elgin we had been on the road for six months. George's jaw was pretty well healed and we went to living in a tent behind Aunt Josie's place. We lived in a tent all winter and the only thing that kept us alive was bread and the seven sacks of dried apples.

That spring Dad got a job driving sawdust cart at the mill. We built a ramshackle house with rough-cut lumber and settled down. I hoped this was the last time we would ever move. It wasn't, and a few years later it was back in the wagon — to homestead ground on Smith Mountain. I think some men were just born to wander, my dad was one.

The reason we cut away from the trail in Wyoming was so Dad could find work. We traveled here and there and Dad eventually caught on with a sheep ranch south of Bozeman, Montana.

We tried to travel again but our horses were in sad shape. Dad sold them and the wagon and purchased tickets on the train.

All I remember about the train ride was a boy coming through at a stop selling paper cones of Bing cherries. Dad bought one for my brother and me to share and I ended up staining the front of my new white dress with bright red cherry juice.

When we got to Hillsboro, Oregon, Grandpa Henry Harrison Byers was there to welcome us. He was a carpenter by trade and had been the one to write Dad and encourage us to join him.

Dad went to work in a sawmill and we lived in one spot two years. We were poor as churchmice and Dad decided to try something else — farming. We loaded again and moved to the Goodnough Hills in Washington.

Dad drove along the Columbia River and at the mouth of Rock Creek we turned north. At the Mobley homestead, above the breaks of the Columbia, we stopped. They were giving up and moving elsewhere more promising. We bought their place.

Our family needed a saddle horse so we could get around and one of the Mobley boys sold us his before he left. Brother Art took a trial run, after Mobleys were gone, down to the breaks near the Indian settlement.

Art was riding nice and easy when he spotted half a dozen Indians riding at top speed toward him. He got scared, turned for home and let the horse unwind.

As it all turned out the Indians weren't after Art. They were after the Mobley boy who had owned the horse; they had mistaken Art for him. The Mobley boy was wanted for pulling a practical joke on an Indian named John Teehee. John was old, close to a hundred at the time. The boy had switched gunpowder for tobacco in filling the old Indian's pipe and later when John Teehee went to have a smoke, the pipe blew up in his face. It burned his hair and blistered his face.

After that we became acquainted with John Teehee and he started appearing at our place in the mornings. He would sit down on the bench at the kitchen table and sometimes Mother would not know he was there until she turned around and saw him. We ate plain — eggs, graham bread and milk from the cow Dad tended. John ate just what we did, no more, no less.

One breakfast John came in saying, ''Papooses go ki-i-i-i, they got nothing eat, days, days.''

Only the old and young had stayed behind in the Indian settlement, the rest of the group had traveled to Yakima to gather berries. Mother fixed a basket of food — biscuits we called graham jams, bacon and eggs. The old Indian took it back to the papooses.

Before the main body of Indians went huckleberrying one buck we knew, Kinapoo, had come to the house. He carried under his arm two deerskins. They were rolled up tight. He asked if Father would store them for him until he returned. Father put them away in the attic.

We never looked to see what was inside the skins and after the best part of a month Kinapoo and his squaw came to the house. Kinapoo was about 25 years old and was educated at a white man's school in Oregon; his wife spoke only Indian. Kinapoo asked for his deerskins; Father took them down and handed them to Kinapoo. The squaw made motions and Kinapoo asked if we would like to see what was rolled in the leather.

The squaw unrolled one of the skins — all it contained was a pair of small beaded moccasins. These she held to her breast. She cried and wailed, ''Papoose Memaloose, Papoose Memaloose.''

My father's name — Charles Macy. He was a buckaroo in Wyoming and ran horses on the open range. Supported Mother and five kids on what he could round up; he sold the young horses, turned the mares back.

At the tail end of summer Mother and Dad had a talk. She told him this was no kind of life for us kids; he had to agree and thereupon we got ready to move to Oregon. Mother had a sister living in Forest Grove and our destination became Aunt Emma's house.

Dad made a cover over the box of our farm wagon with bows and canvas. We took off with no loose stock, just four horses — two as a team, two tied on behind the wagon.

The first day we were on the road we came across a sheet metal stove lying in the middle of nowhere and Mother insisted we take it. She argued that it would cut down on cooking chores. Dad built a platform on the back of the wagon and set the stove there, tying it on. Every morning he tied the same knots and each night undid them and set the stove on the ground.

We used sagebrush most of the way to fire the stove and ate whatever we could kill. My older brother Clarence shot prairie chickens and we kids used to run down jackrabbits. We took turns running one around in circles; when he was tired he slowed down and whoever was behind him then would pop a stick behind his ears.

I was six years old and could do most anything. I hunted back and forth in front of the wagon — I've seen bird dogs do the same. If I found anything of interest I yelled for Pa. He would come and take a look at a dead cow, furniture or a discarded wagon part. Sometimes if the wheel I found was better than one we were traveling on, he would swap. Our wagon seemed to have a penchant for trouble with wheels. We lost hour after hour repairing spokes or pushing back the rim.

Coming along Snake River an Indian rode alongside and asked Pa if he would like to trade horses. He had a good-looking cayuse and Pa offered him our spare team which was wore down and pretty well shot. The Indian never said a word, just got down, put his blanket on one of our horses and rode away leading the other. We had his horse, he had ours.

It was almost three months to the day from Glenrock, Wyoming, until we landed in Forest Grove, Oregon. Aunt Emma came running out of the house drying her hands on her apron; she was tickled pink.

The rest of the afternoon neighbors came over to offer welcome and all the kids around there got together a rodeo; we rode calves and boy were they buckers!

That night I picked stickers from my arms and legs and went to bed beneath the wagon. We stayed there, behind Aunt Emma's, for a good long while until Dad finally found us a farm.

Dear Diary,

My name is Mae Stone, thirteen years old.
We are traveling west by wagon and several
relatives come with us.

Today is July 10, 1898. The wind blew in our face all day today, dust was thick. Nothing exciting happened except on our way to Thousand Springs Uncle Ress killed 5 sage hens. We ate them for dinner.

(11th) Today it was nice traveling. In the morning, though, pretty chilly, we made 13 miles and before the day was over, made 25. In the afternoon I rode Gene. Once, when I got a ways from the wagon a bunch of cattle chased me. I rode up to our wagon and those cattle followed for several miles. I wasn't scared in the least.

(12th) It rained on us. We saw sage hens and heard coyotes howl. We made 25 miles for the second day in a row.

(13th) Today Papa saw 10 antelope but couldn't get a shot. We stayed in camp until 10 o'clock to let the horses rest a little. Uncle Ress fell off Gene this morning. We stopped about 3 when we came across grass and water. There is a creek here and an old log cabin where we camped. Papa caught 6 trout. We ate them.

(14th) We camped early today and the colt, Brigham, is quite tired. A cowboy was camped nearby and came over on his way to get wood. He is the first person we have seen in four days. Another just came by. That makes 2. The second cowboy said he had come 70 miles in order to get poles to make a hayrack. According to him we are but 90 miles from the Snake River.

(15th) Brigham could hardly walk today so in the morning we let him ride in the wagon. After awhile we took him out, put him in again after dinner. He was quiet as a lamb. Seen 5 antelopes this morning and a ''Bull Fight,'' too. Camped beside a hot spring and the water was so hot that we made coffee and drank it right out of the ground.

(Sunday, 16th) Came as far as Rock Creek. Had dinner. Rock Creek is farming country. Passed through a little town and saw girls and boys walking to church. We hauled Brigham all afternoon and Papa killed a rattlesnake today, 8 rattles. I saw one but it was small. There are lots of horned toads up here. Uncle Ress went fishing but didn't get a bite. While he was gone the horses broke their picket line and Papa had to run about a mile to catch them.

(17th) We left Rock Creek at 10 minutes past 6 and traveled 29 miles on the Oregon Trail. The horses are pretty tired. We hauled Brigham for 3 hours today. The going was all up and down hills. We are pretty tired, too, and had to make dry camp for noon. Papa and Uncle Ress tried to get hay for the horses from some old man down the road but he was so mean you couldn't talk to him. Ask him a question, he would only grunt. The road today was awful rocky. We came to the Snake River at Lewis's Ferry and 2 women brought us over. Their men were away working. We had to help them when we got stuck on a sand bar. We pushed it off. Brigham wouldn't ride on the ferry, he swam with the horses. Water came up to the horses' bellys and poor Brigham had to walk on his hind legs to keep his head out. We passed an old fort today, all fallen down. It looked to be one used in the '50s. I didn't get any arrows. We came 15 miles with no water to drink. We got dry before we got here.

(18th) Papa fished the Snake River and caught a salmon, our first. While he was away from camp I wrote a letter to Addie. We left Snake River after dinner and traveled until we crossed 5 miles of sand. The horses were weary to the bone when we finally stopped. They eat only hay and look poor. We made but 12 miles today. At least the mosquitoes here are not quite as bad as they were down near the river. They nearly would eat you up down there. We slept out by the side of the wagon and the moon shone on us. We broke camp before the sun was up and before the moon had set.

(19th) The horses sweat horribly and I am afraid they will not make it. We came to the town, Bliss. It is surrounded for miles and miles with sand and the last hill coming into town is steep, rocky. The horses tried to play out on us. We ate dinner in Bliss and bought hay for the horses, some wheat. The wheat we mixed with their oats to make the oats go further. I am writing this in the sagebrush with the campfire for a light (we are cooking beans.) Knocked off 17 miles today. Camped with 2 other wagons. They belong to the same outfit.

(20th) We follow the two wagons up Kingdom Hill and it isn't as bad as we had thought, although it is quite steep. Coming down Sal went to kick a fly off her flank and broke her harness. But Papa fixed it. Hay we found was selling for half-dollar a hundred weight. We bought 25 cents worth. Brigham did alright riding only 1 hour and a boy making the trip, Harry, took off his shoes and walked barefooted. It is over 100 degrees in the shade. Horses — worn, sand is soft. We are going to sleep in a tent. Made 22 miles.

(21st) It is Friday and we left the old camping ground early this morning, went way out on the prairie among the lava rocks to eat our dinner. It was a dry camp, no water. After dinner the other wagons followed us down through a canyon and past a few small farms. We pull up at about 2 in the afternoon to let the horses rest. The other wagons went on ahead, their stock being in better shape than ours. Three wagons and a band of cayuse horses came through camp heading to Wyoming. The people driving them came from Oregon, lived there for 6 years, but are giving up. Brigham's hind feet are awful sore today. We had to tie rags on his feet so he could walk. Papa only let him ride a little today and all of us had to stay out of the wagon. We were too much for the horses. Papa bought some Timothy hay tonight, came back in from fishing the creek with two nice trout. We made 21 miles today.

(22nd) Four other wagons camped near us and also last night we got a half-pound of cherries. Mother paid 10 cents for them and they were as sour as could be. I rode Gene nearly all day and feel pretty sore now. We did 20 miles. Part way we saw a cowboy with a whole lot of cattle and horses he was driving. The cowboy tried to head them around us. His horse was going as fast as it could and right beside us his horse fell and the cowboy came down hopping on his hands and knees like an old bull frog. I guess it didn't hurt him.

(23rd) We left with the four wagons, in the rear, but we soon got in the middle. We stopped for dinner and when we started again we were lead. We reached Boise and lost the rest of them somewhere behind us. Brigham has sore feet tonight and to make things worse he got tangled up in some rope and skinned his hind leg. Along the way saw a real live fist-to-fist fight. It was over a horse and between a boy, and a girl. Tonight we are camped on the edge of Boise. Uncle Ress went downtown.

(24th) Papa bought provisions and had Gene's front feet reshod. We came 10 miles out from Boise and are camped in a pasture of someone's. I don't know their name but they are milking a lot of cows and separating the cream and selling it to the creamery. I wrote to Grandmother today but did not have a chance to mail it. The mosquitoes are pretty thick and so are the flies.

(25th) We were nearly eaten up by mosquitoes last night and now today the flies are tormenting us. It is hot. We are just lying around today letting the horses rest. Got a box of green apples. Papa traded the mare and Brigham off for a brown work horse. The colt was too near given out to travel much farther. The work horse is a gentle one.

(26th) We left the ranch where we had been laying over and made 30 miles in a hurry. The new horse is pretty fast and was so fresh that they stepped off the miles in a hurry. We were in the awfulest sand storm today, the sand blowing until you couldn't see a thing. Papa killed a coyote.

(27th) We left the sand hole about 6 o'clock this morning and met up with 2 wagons. We traveled together until noon and then left them. They were laying over on account of a sick horse. We crossed the Snake River at Nyssa Ferry and camped tonight in Oregon for the first time on Malheur River. Made 30 miles.

(28th) We struck the Old Government Road this morning and followed it until we got to Vale then took the Willow Creek Road. I rode Gene all afternoon until he laid down and refused to go farther. In camp tonight there is wind and lightning flashes. I was blinded twice. We made 30 miles, again.

(29th) Horses were frisky to go this morning. Traveled 26 miles. We are camped in an old house tonight. We put the horses in the pasture, there is good feed. No one lives in the house.

(Sunday, 30th) We left the old deserted house and came a ways down Willow Creek where we camped for dinner. There was one wagon where we stopped, laying over for repairs. It was an old man and old woman. Tonight we are camped in a little grove of trees, with good water and feed and out of the mosquitoes. We saw a cow today that looked exactly like the one we started this trip with. I think it was her and have no idea how she stayed ahead of us. We did not try to catch her. Made 20 miles.

(31st) We went 15 miles around a hill today and straight across we gained only 2. It was uphill today, nice and cool. A lady from a ranch around here came to camp. She offered us sweet milk, buttermilk and some cream for our coffee. She says that they milk 12 cows, have ten others and 20 head of calves. Half of them are orphan. We made 25 miles today which was pretty good, it was all uphill.

(1st day of August) Met a band of sheep up in good grass country. There were maybe 2,000 in the band and only one man and three dogs to take care of them. Tonight we are camped by the side of a river or creek, I don't know which. The horses want to wander off tonight probably because we traveled through timber all day. It was nice and cool, I could smell the ground.

(2nd) We crossed over Dixie Mountain and it was awful steep, but not as bad as some others we have crossed. We caught up with one wagon today and traveled all day together. Got to Prairie City and got some stuff to eat and pulled out about three miles to camp. Two outfits passed us. We made 23 miles.

(3rd) Went to John Day today and got supplies. Camped on the river. Judge threw a shoe and Papa had to have him reshod. In the wagon camped beside us tonight is a woman 64 years old. We made 23 miles today.

(4th) We are camped in an old man's field. He is a bachelor and to be friendly gave us some sweet milk. We got ahold of some huckleberries and I almost stepped on a rattlesnake but Uncle Ress killed it. We bought some cherries today and came through Dayville. 23 miles.

(5th) We had awful rocky and steep hills to climb. It was up and down all day. We walked and walked and now my feet are blistered and sore. I am nearly given out. The water in the river felt good. I didn't wade, I didn't have the strength. I sat down and now feel much better because of it. There is an old widow woman living near where we are camped. She came down and gave us sweet and buttermilk. She is pretty well fixed having sheep and a milk cow.

(6th) We left the campground and went past the old widow lady. She gave us a dog, he followed all day. 16 miles. Met a man on horseback today and he talked so zig crazy that we all had to laugh at him. Tonight we pulled into some man's hayfield. Up here at the edge of the field, back in the timber, we have a perfect camping spot. There is spring water cold as ice and the men caught 21 fish. We laid over from afternoon on and I washed a lot of dirty clothes, and they were good and dirty, too.

(7th) We are in camp lying around this afternoon. Our dog I was so proud of must have went home. He stayed through the night but disappeared this morning. The men shot their rifles and then went and bought two small hams. Boiled one whole today. Did some more washing. Got started late but still did 20 miles.

(8th) The men got up early today and went hunting. Got 5 ducks and a sage hen. A sheepherder gave us some mutton. His sheep camp is in the middle of someone's hayfield. We stayed there — 17 miles today.

(9th) Traveled 23 miles today. Road was good but there was a cold rain and the wind blew, we were miserable. I was afraid I would fall asleep and freeze. I might still.

(10th) We left that alfalfa field where we were camped. It rained all night and all morning. We are chilled to the bone. Got into Prineville and I mailed a letter to Grandmother. Got one from her. We bought provisions in town and pulled on 12 miles and camped in an old sand hole.

(11th) Stopped along the Deschutes River for dinner and the men caught one trout. Where we are camped there are 4 other outfits. One of them gave us a dog. He is a shepherd. Made 23 miles today, in places had sand up to the spokes.

(12th) The 4 wagons went our way and we fell in with them, until we got past the tollgate. Coming through the gate it cost us $2 for the team and 20 cents for Gene. All day we travel through timber. We found a nice black dog today, no owner around, and took him. We are blessed with 2 dogs. Made 18 miles today. Camped at wonderful spot in the timber, all alone.

(13th, Sunday again) We had a bad day today, it rained on us and was so cold we froze. We came to the summit of the Cascade Mountains and crossed over. We traveled most of the time in sand but the worst was coming down hill. There is lava rock on top. We seen 1 great big, burned-out crater and a lot of smaller ones. We are camped under a shed by Fish Lake. Our house has 2 sides and 1 end. We built the fire in the opposite end and it almost smoked us to death. Uncle Ress caught 20 fish and Papa caught 1. There are quite a few people camped around here. Some came from 40 miles the other side of Prineville to pick wild blackberries. We came only 16 miles today.

(14th) We are laying over today and it has not quit raining for one minute. The men fished Clear Lake and Papa came back with a great big fish.

(15th) We left Fish Lake and traveled down the muddiest road you ever saw. We passed a lot of berry pickers, went past Mountain House and traveled on the edge of an old landslide. Camped at Lower Soda. According to the sign boards we came 21 miles.

(16th) Left Lower Soda Springs and traveled until dark over the slippery and muddy roads. It was hard on the team. Twice Prince slipped and fell to his knees but was able to get up on his own. We got down near Sweet Home and asked directions. After some difficulty we found the ranch. We had dinner by candlelight. We were wet, cold and cranky and as soon as we ate we went to the barn and went to sleep in the hay.

The End

Mae Stone

We had two of the finest mules that ever lived — Jenny, a bay and Jack, an iron gray. They pulled us cross country to Elgin, Oregon.

I grew up with the mules and I didn't care for Jenny, but Jack — now Jack I cared for a whole bunch. He was easy to catch and easy to ride. I used to swing on his tail, between his legs. He was that gentle.

The summer I was eight Daddy had me out working the potato patch with him. We were cultivating, Daddy running the double-shovel plow and me riding Jack. My job was to keep the team from stepping on the rows of potatoes.

I don't know what spooked Jack and caused the accident but I always supposed he saw a rattlesnake. We had a lot around Elgin.

Jack reared and came down kicking. That broke his belly band and it pulled the harness to the inside, me with it. Jack was scared, Jenny was scared and they took off running.

The force of Jack's kick set Daddy on the ground. He had no opportunity to stop the runaway. He yelled ''whoa'' at the top of his lungs. That was all he could do.

I was slipping down the side of Jack, holding on to the hames and harness for all I was worth. Jenny and Jack were running fast as they could. They bumped against one another and me in between.

The harness gave gradual, rolling me under Jack where his hind legs hit me on the back and threw dirt clods in my face — directly behind was the double-shovel plow bouncing along.

I don't know when I gave up. It wasn't a conscious effort, my strength just disappeared. Jack avoided stepping on me but the plow went over the top. It cut me across the stomach, from hip to hip.

Daddy carried me to the house. He sent for Doc Cobb and when he got there all he could do was sew me back together and hope infection didn't set in. I don't know how many stitches he took but I am sure it was well over a hundred.

I was lucky 'cause I should have been cut in two but I never let the accident bother me and I sure never held it against Jack.

Jack had such a good disposition, was such a good-looking iron gray that I never thought about his leaving the family until the day Daddy came home with a team of young horses. He had traded Jenny and Jack. I bawled my eyes out.

My folks came west on a train and stopped in La Grande, Oregon. They were looking for homestead land. Dad rounded up a team of horses, got a wagon and headed for the only land available — Wallowa Valley.

I was born there in 1892. Two years later Mother caught typhoid, died; when I was five, Father passed away.

No one wanted all eight of us children so we were taken one by one. I went to the Rineharts, Lew and Ella. They were generous people and accustomed to having stray children in their home.

I kept track of my family by news I heard. My oldest brother took a harvest job over the mountains but he drowned while swimming in the Walla Walla. My oldest sister contracted TB and died.

I stayed with the Rineharts and after the winters of 1904 and '05 Mr. Rinehart was sick of the snow and cold and said we were moving to a milder climate. He spoke of the Willamette Valley.

About this time a young man came to live with us. His name was Bert Dexter. He was six years older than I but we fell in love; we promised that someday we would marry.

Mr. Rinehart found the land he was looking for in the Willamette Valley — Yamhill County — and came home to get us. He prepared the wagon while Bert and I brought the horses in off the range.

We left Wallowa County with a four-horse team, a wagon and six head of loose mustangs which Bert and I drove. The horse I was mounted on was the bell horse. I led, Bert brought up the rear.

The first day we reached Tollgate at the top of the Blues just at dark. They were closed for winter but one old fellow was still stationed there and he let us use the barn. We hayed our horses and slept in the loft.

Next morning we were on the road early and hit the old Oregon Trail outside Pendleton. The going was rough on account of the farmers hauling wagons of wheat over it; chuckholes everywhere.

One day to Echo and three more to the John Day River. As we started to cross, a farmer on the opposite side waved us off and motioned to go farther downstream where the crossing was better. For that time of year the water was high; Bert took the bell off my horse, tied it around his saddle horn and led the loose horses into the water.

I watched to make sure he was safely on the other side before I entered the river. My horse was a short-legged pony and I had to hold my feet in the air to keep from getting wet but I didn't have a bit of trouble.

Once we were safely across a dog commenced to barking on the opposite side. It was our dog Charlie. Charlie had a habit of riding in the wagon and whenever it stopped he jumped down and scouted the neighborhood. That is what he had done and had failed to climb back in before we crossed. But good ol' Charlie wasn't going to be left, he jumped in the river and swam to us. Just his little head stuck out of the water.

At The Dalles we loaded everything aboard a big sternwheel ferry. It was like something I had never seen — a boat so large! Of course neither Bert nor I had been out of Wallowa County before.

As we came down the Columbia Gorge it started raining and it rained all the way to Portland. Portland then was a small town; Mr. Rinehart found a livery stable near the dock where we left the horses and we went uptown and stayed in a hotel. We ate at a Chinese restaurant that evening and later all of us were sick.

The next morning Mr. Rinehart still had a bad stomach but he insisted we start. It rained every mile of the way and we pulled into Yamhill after dark. Mr. Rinehart was the only one to have already seen the place; he had been there when he bought it. Before long we were away from town and beyond houses where we could ask directions. There were no lights; the night was dark and the rain came hard.

We traveled to foothills and began climbing. Dense brush and trees surrounded the narrow road. At night such a compressed mass of vegetation was eerie. I couldn't tell what the end of my nose was doing and then behind the trees and in the brush I saw miniature flashes. I thought they were glowing cigarettes.

Bert had taken over driving the wagon for sick Mr. Rinehart and since I was alone in back with the horses I pushed them until they crowded behind the wagon. The mud was so thick we could hardly get through and as I drove the mustangs close they pinched the team. The grade was exceedingly steep and one of the wheelers went down and could not get up. Bert and Mr. Rinehart yelled at me to keep the mustangs back and they climbed down in the mud, unharnessed the wheeler so she could get to her feet.

We continued on and passed through a little valley where there was grass and plenty of it. The mustangs I was driving were raised in eastern Oregon and had never seen a shoot of green grass — they stopped and no way in the world could I keep those horses moving. I dropped behind and didn't like that on account of I could still see cigarettes glowing in the dark. I figured they were tramps hiding from us.

When we pulled into the yard of our new home I only had one horse besides mine with me — that was Bert's saddle horse. The rest were scattered up and down the road feeding on grass.

The wagon rolled to a stop after crossing a yard of apples. The ground was covered with apples; the horses put their heads down and started chomping.

Mr. Rinehart broke in the front door to the house — he didn't have a key. There was not a stick of furniture inside but there was wood in the woodshed and Bert started a fire in the great rock fireplace. We warmed ourselves and I said I was sure glad we were there. I told them about the tramps and seeing their cigarettes burning. Mr. Rinehart laughed, he told me I just learned what a firefly was.

Bert and I unhitched the team and put them away in one of the two huge barns that were on the property. Then we went back to look for the mustangs. As we rode, Bert rang the bell; the mustangs nickered from quite a ways away and came running. We brought them back to the barn, rubbed them down and put hay and grain in the manger. By then it was midnight and Bert and I were soaked clear through to the bone. We went inside the house and the Rineharts had it nice and warm, there was a lantern lit and it seemed somewhat like home. We slept on the hearth in front of the fire that night and little did I know that three years later, standing in front of that great stone fireplace, Bert Dexter and I would be married.

We left Iowa in early spring and it was fall when we saw Seattle. We was a long time coming. Pa bought a little place about ten miles from town but I think the constant rain got to him and the next year we started back to Iowa for a visit. To pay the way we trailed a band of wild horses.

It was Pa, Ma and sister Jane in the wagon with two or three horses tied on and me driving the rest on my Shetland pony, Pet. At Snake River the ferry was up about eight miles from where I crossed. I drove the horses into the water while Pa took the ferry and then we met down the road.

The weather stayed hot every day and I was trapped in a cloud of dust, if not from the horses, then from the wagon. We moved pretty fast and along the way Pet developed a kink in his neck and I had to shoot him. But in Iowa we sold every horse we had for $125 a head and that was a whole lot more than we had in them.

When we started west again I was driving a wagon of my own and in Wyoming a bunch of renegades stampeded our horses. It was five days before all our teams showed up and by then we were low on food. The others went on but I stayed to help an old crippled man, who had been camped with us, find his horses. That took three days more and it was a week before I caught up with our other two wagons.

I don't know why, we had already lived in Washington and hadn't liked it, but that is where we were headed until the accident coming out of the Blue Mountains. Pa's team started acting up, bucking and kicking. We was on steep hill ground and in order to save what he had Pa overturned the wagon against the bank; when I stopped to help, my team took off and tore my wagon to pieces.

After that we went back to the last valley we had passed through; Summerville, Oregon, became our home.

When we made the crossing from Nebraska with the wagon and top buggy I was nine years old and rode every bit of the way on my own horse Logan. We had twelve other head of horses and along the way a mare foaled. We were several days letting her take it easy and waiting for the little fellow so as he could keep up.

A group of freighters overtook us and they saw the mare and colt. They stopped us and asked if we were interested in making a trade. The railroad had come through and forced them out of business. They were looking to trade mules and get in the horse-raising business.

Father gave up two mares and the colt for a pair of mules, one named Babe and the other Fanny. They were good mules, broke to lead. We put them on the wagon my brother drove and they were smarter than he was. My brother had a habit of falling asleep and if we were going downhill Babe and Fanny would move off the road to loose dirt, help slow down some. Everytime that happened my brother would wake up thinking he had a runaway. It was comical.

Even though I rode Logan all the way I still had to help with the wagons. Evenings I unhitched the teams and tended to them; the tent had to be set up and the cook stove readied for dinner. Mother and her sister slept in the tent and we cooked outside unless it was raining, then we moved inside the tent.

One time we traveled all day in the rain. I was cold to the bone and guess that I fell asleep in the saddle. When I woke I couldn't tell where I was — I had no idea. But as it turned out Father had wrapped me in a canvas and put me inside the tent behind the warm stove.

I remember we camped on the main street of Boise and then headed out across eastern Oregon. We didn't see a soul from the time we left Boise until we hit the toll station on top of the Cascades.

We wintered on a farm out of Brownsville and all of our horses died, even Logan. It was alkali poisoning from coming across the trail that killed them. If it hadn't been for the freight mules we would never have been able to farm that spring. Babe and Fanny pulled the plow — they were immune to alkali.

We left Missouri in the spring of the year with two teams and wagons and it was not until October that we made our last camp of the trail. Last camp was special; we stopped before dark in a swale with a creek running through. There were no trees, just sagebrush and rocks. The next day we made it to our destination, the Killmar's homestead. Dad had gone to school with Mr. Killmar and there were other friends from home who had settled nearby, John Seger and Johnny Schrader.

They had all come to Idaho early and taken homesteads but by the time we arrived the homestead land was gone. If we wanted a farm we had to buy one. We had no money.

Dad looked for work and finally caught on with a freight company hauling from the Clearwater River back into the gold country: Florence, Elk City, Buffalo Hump. Dad was a duck out of water; he was a flatlander but he knew how to handle horses.

Years later he used to tell me about his freighting days: "One time I was taking a load of live hogs up to Elk City. It was cold and rainy and the hogs were a mite uncomfortable. Dark overtook me so I stopped and made camp. I always carried kerosene so I could start a fire and that was the first thing I did.

"The hogs kept up steady squealing. They were making quite a fuss. I built the fire big. There was a circle of light maybe twenty-five feet around me and that night I heard every meat-eating animal in the woods. Cougar and bear came right to the fire. I could see the green and yellow of their eyes and hear them growl low under their breath.

"Morning eventually came and I put on the coffee and started breakfast. By the time I finished the sun was up and I felt a little better knowing the animals were back in their lairs. I took one team down to the creek for water. The trail was muddy and I watched my step. At the creek the horses shied, snorted and blew. They were skittish and so excited they drove me into the creek before I could line them around.

"Coming up the trail they shied again and this time I could see why. There in the soft mud, over the top of my heel print, was the track of a cougar.

"There was another time I had a run-in with a cougar. I was coming back to Clearwater River along the canyon where the road drops away on one side to nothing.

"I was at that point when my lead team got frightened. They were wary of the road ahead and tried to jackknife. Like I already said, there was only one place for me to go and that was over the cliff. I threw the whip out and by popping just the right piece of horseflesh I kept them in line. By then all the horses were scared.

"Out of the corner of my eye I caught sight of a cougar crouching on the bank side of the road. The cougar moved slowly. Only with the whip and the grace of God was I able to maintain control. The horses wanted to jackknife and run, I applied the majority of my attention to the lead team.

"The cougar leaped onto a stump beside the wagon. I could have reached over and petted him on the head but I was too busy. That cat went into a frenzy, ripping off bark with his claws. He hissed and spat at both me and the horses.

"At that point the horses had taken about all they would. They started moving ahead quickly and I let them run as long as they wanted. When we finally stopped I had no hat on my head and I didn't go back after it."

Dad always liked to tell about his freighting days but at heart he was a farmer. The only reason he was a freighter was in order to earn money enough to buy land. After two years driving freight our old friend George Killmar got hold of Dad. He said a relative of his was giving up his homestead, he was homesick for Missouri.

Dad paid five hundred dollars for a quarter section on Big Butte near the Killmars. It was the highest point on the prairie and looked over Seven Devils country. The back side of the property was cut by Lawyer Canyon.

I suppose you would have to call the homestead marginal and the one-room cabin on it was not much either. We added on a lean-to for sleeping. There was a fireplace and that was about all.

First thing added to the farm was a barn. Dad always took care of stock first. Then there was a hen house, a smoke house and a cow barn.

After living in the homestead cabin for six years Dad built us a house. He used rough lumber and then, and only then, did it seem we had settled down, found a home.

One of the horses that brought us west was named Dick. He was a black gelding and oh, but I loved Dick — nothing was too good for him. I used to sneak him grain, I would put extra handfuls under his hay and Dad never caught me. I wanted Dick to fill out that little hollow spot on his hip. I loved him that much.

When I started to school at the Big Butte schoolhouse I rode Dick. We didn't have a barn there so when I got to school I would take off the bridle and let him find his own way home. From inside I watched him traveling the mile and a half. Sometimes he would race home, trying to avoid a storm. In the spring and summer, when the weather was part way decent, Dick just poked along. He visited with every horse and it might take him until noon to reach home.

Two days after the start of school, when I was eleven years old, I walked home from school as usual. I went in the house and fixed a jelly sandwich and then came out to watch Mother. She was breaking bones and grinding them for the chickens. The bone helped the chickens lay eggs with good shells.

We always hunted animal bones in Lawyer Canyon on the back side of the homestead. There were bones among the rocks in the canyon and we brought them home.

On that day in 1906 I was standing watching Mother and eating my jelly sandwich. Mother was chopping bones into bits with an ax and then running them through the grinder. She chopped into a leg bone and at the same instant something hit my eye. It blinded me and knocked me down. My eyelid was cut and a piece of bone had gone into my eye. It was terrible — the pain.

Doctor Busey from Clearwater was visiting a neighbor dying with pneumonia and Dad went and got him. Doc Busey put a black patch over my eye to keep out the light but I already knew that my eye was gone. Dad took me to the doctor in Spokane. I got an artificial eye.

I didn't return to school that year until after Christmas, and the hardest part about going back was realizing that I would be the way I was the rest of my life.

A couple years went by. We were right in the middle of wheat harvest when wet weather hit and Dad told the threshing crew they could sleep in the barn. One of the men took sick — real sick — and Dad ran him into Grangeville. Right away the doctor said it was diphtheria. Dad asked him about us children, whether we were exposed but the doctor said the diphtheria was past the infectious stage.

Monday morning all us children, the school teacher who boarded with us, and Mother were sick. The symptoms were diphtheria. Dad refused to go back to the doctor in Grangeville after he had been given a bum steer so he called Doc Busey at Clearwater. In no time flat he was there in his buggy.

"I'm going to have to have anti-toxin and right away," Doc Busey told my oldest brother Ed over the telephone. Ed was in Grangeville and immediately he picked up the anti-toxin and headed for our place. By the time he delivered the medicine his horse had been run in the ground.

We were sick as people can get and still be alive. Dad refused to come down with diphtheria. He said he had to take care of us and to ward off the infection he ate handfuls of sulfur and smoked Grangeville twist tobacco in a pipe. Doc Busey had recommended he do both and it must have worked because Dad never was sick.

We eventually got over the diphtheria but Mother's house plants never did. When the fumigators came in and sprayed down the place they killed every plant in the house.

It took a long while for the inside to look normal but Mother took cuttings from neighbors. The plants grew and time slipped away. In the barn my sweetheart Dick had gotten old. He was 27, which is old for a horse, and I could no longer ride him; he could not bear my weight. Then he quit eating and it was so sad. Poor Dick, all skin and bone.

Just behind our house was Lawyer Canyon. It was deep and rocky. We never had to bury dead animals, we just threw them into Lawyer Canyon. A cousin came over to our house one day and when I saw him with a rifle in hand and Dick by the halter — I knew.

I sat on the back porch and watched them walk out of sight toward Lawyer Canyon. I waited what seemed like hours. Dick was such a pretty black gelding, nothing was too good for Dick. Then, a single shot and I saw Dick in my mind — rolling and rolling.

My cousin came walking back alone, with the halter slung over his shoulder. As he passed he patted me on the head and then he hung up the halter, went inside and had coffee with Mom and Dad.

Promise Land

I learned from the Oregon Trail to accept fate, live one day at a time. As I grew older, I looked around and what I saw was the folks' place at Grand Ronde. It could barely support one family. I was offered a job in the woods and took it.

That first logging I did was in the Nestucca River drainage. I worked there better than six months and in fall drifted to Portland for a look at city life.

Spring came, sun replaced the rain and it was like being freed from jail. Bit by a wander bug I crossed the Cascades and was into the Deschutes area before I found work. The job was with Keel Brothers and I bumped knots. What was good about working for Keel Brothers is once they knew I was sticking they let me rotate and learn all the jobs in the trade. They were a fine outfit and I put thirty years in with them.

Then came the early spring which I would just as soon forget. Snow still lay in scattered patches as we felled timber along the Little Deschutes River. One afternoon the sky blackened and buckets of water poured down. With the Little Deschutes on the rise I directed the men to use their peaveys and get our logs in the water. In the space of a few hours we had everything in sight floating.

Some yellow pine floats, some doesn't. Sinkers created a bottleneck at the bottom of a short series of fast water. I sized a bad situation and as foreman I knew the responsibility was mine.

One log causes a jam and it is that same log that frees it. What I had to do was find the log, set it free and run like hell.

From shore someone yelled, ''Joe, let her be. We'll blow her. Joe, can you hear me?'' Of course I could but I listened with only one ear, I had to concentrate on what I was doing. A log jam can be safe one instant, not the next — the difference between alive and dead.

Climbing over the pile I located the key log, wedged in front of maybe a couple hundred yellow pine. I moved the key like a person might play with dynamite. I rolled it slightly, gently worked the combination, the peavey guided by my strength.

In my head I knew what to do and bit by bit I gained. A roar was in the air as the backed-up water fought its way through the jam. I pried and pulled the key log and ever so slightly it moved. Then suddenly it came easy. I lost my balance and fell over backwards, came up running. The log jam had broke.

It is a cardinal sin for a logger to be separated from his peavey but I gave mine no thought. From one wet log to another, caulked boot biting bark, and I was always looking ahead for a stationary foothold. I heard someone yell ''Joe'' and it held there in the damp air and then was washed away by the roar of logs coming apart.

They say a man about to die has life pass by in front of him like a picture show. What I saw were the days of our wagon crossing and Cal telling me a story about stopping a buffalo stampede.

"There was a brown swell like it come out of the sea. Buffalo! I brought the wagons in tight as we could and as the buffalo herd came on us I directed the men fire a volley at the point of the charge. Yessir, we shot so many of 'em down that they formed a wall with their bodies. The herd passed on either side."

I was still running, climbing over logs and for half an instant I believed the logs might part like the buffalo had. Then a log turned as I stepped and I couldn't pull my caulks. Water nipped at my toes — my ankles were wet — knees and then I was pulled under. I looked just as I went down and all I could see was an avalanche of logs. Two logs bounced together, pinning my leg and pushing me underwater.

From a great distance I felt warmth against my face — the feel of sunshine in January. I opened my eyes to a fire. I was seated, wrapped in blankets and propped with butt cuts under my arms and back.

"Settle down, Joe," someone told me. "Your leg is busted. You'll be all right."

I had no feeling in my right leg and I eased the blankets back for a look. What greeted me was a bloody mess. Bone, gristle, meat — it was hard to grasp it was mine. When I did I lost consciousness.

There is no way to tell how much time went by, I dreamed, then awoke to clean sheets and a dinner tray. I knew I was not at logging camp and was right — I was in the Bend hospital.

Again I dreamed and woke staring at my right foot, it pushed covers like a mountain pushes sky. It was there, still there, I had my foot! I had expected it to be gone.

"You're tough as nails, Joe. You can walk again if you set your mind to it; but your logging days are through," the doctor told me.

I thought about that. Now a buckaroo who gets hurt can always wrangle or feed hay. And a fisherman who loses his boat can go to work for someone else. But what in the hell is a washed-up logger going to do?

The doctor was looking at me, waiting for my reaction.

"I guess," I told him, "I'm going to get in a lot of fishing."

When John Thogerson and I married we took the first job that came along. That was on a ranch up at Sherman County, Oregon. John was a ranch hand and got $35 a month, I cooked for $15 and that meant getting up at four o'clock every morning for breakfast.

We lived in the house with the owner, Johnny Holman. I suppose what kept us going was thinking about a place of our own. John finally traded off a little homestead out of Klickitat, Washington, that he took before we married and with what we had been able to save we bought a place near Dufur on what is known as Center Ridge.

There was a shack and an old Ben Davis apple tree on the property. That was about all. John got hold of another small building and we moved it beside our house so we could have a washroom and woodshed.

We had lots of good neighbors around us, none too close. We were farmers, just plain country people — didn't have much but then we didn't expect much, either.

We were tied to our farm. We had a good team of horses, John raised wheat and I started our family. We had four children born — Rolla, Harold, Melba and Donny.

Donny was my baby. When he was two he came down with pneumonia. We were having a tough year of it, weatherwise, and I guess he didn't stay warm enough.

I did all I could to break the fever but nothing seemed to help. My baby did not respond and we sent to Dufur for Doc Griffith. Over the course of several weeks he made a dozen trips to our place but poor Donny, the doctor could do no good by him.

I was up day and night trying to keep him comfortable. Finally one night Doc Griffith called me aside.

"I'm afraid, Grace, that your son will never live to see morning," he told me. At that point I was completely exhausted from the fight. I had no strength left.

When Doc Griffith left, John told me, "Dear, lie down. I'll stay with him."

He was right, I had to lie down. I was drained, went in and lay on the bed.

I was awake when John came into the room. There was no light. He sat on the edge of the bed, reached out and held my arm.

"I'm sorry," he said, "Donny is no longer with us."

After that I slept. I awoke to a hollowness and have carried it ever since.

Don Gray

We brought Florence, the horse that kicked and broke my jaw, out for a friend — a woman in her mid-twenties who owned her. Her name was Lucy.

By the time we got to Lucy's place in Elgin, Oregon, Lucy had gone and gotten herself married. Down deep she felt guilty about my accident. She got me alone and said, "George, I'm married now and bound to have children. If you will forgive Florence for kicking you and breaking your jaw then we will name our first baby after you."

Well, I told her that was awful nice but when her first child came and he was a boy her husband insisted on naming him after his father, Joseph Bell Scott. When I found out I approached Lucy, "I thought you were going to call him George after me."

"I'm sorry," she told me, "but my husband was determined to name him Joseph Bell."

I was only a kid of eleven but I spoke up and told her that she was either a damn liar or awful forgetful.

"I promise you," she said, "that the next child will be named after you."

It was a girl. But Lucy didn't forget, she named her Georgia. I used to go to the Scott's place and in those days kids had two pairs of diapers. Georgia wore one and the other was washed, rinsed and hanging on a nail back of the stove. Hell, if Georgia had wet ones I changed them, didn't think nothing of it.

When I got a little older I took off looking for perfect country. Snake River, Seven Devils, the desert — all had their drawbacks. The canyons were too deep, the mountains too steep and the desert too dry. After fifteen years of roaming I thought again about Elgin. The country there is a little of all, on the average it isn't bad. I moved home.

I got reacquainted with the Scotts and by then Georgia was a good-looking girl. We talked and I told her that her face sure looked a whole lot prettier than I remembered her backside.

Georgia was a strong Christian, farm-raised. She didn't know nothing about smoking, or drinking, or dancing, or gambling. She didn't go for it.

I was working about twenty miles away from Georgia, up in Wallowa County for Morrison-Knudson. They were building logging roads and I worked seven days a week hauling water for three hundred head of horses. I had my own team to haul with and sometimes in the evenings I came down to Elgin. I guess I was courting.

One time we were in the woods sitting on a stump just talking. I had nervous hands, always have, and to keep them busy I carried a single dice. Like I said before, Georgia was a religious sort.

"What is it?"

"It's a dice, ever see one before?" I asked.

"No, I don't think so. What do you do with it?"

"I settle arguments with it," I told her.

"How does it work?"

"Well," I said, "a couple gets in an argument over some fool thing, chuck the dice. High one wins."

Georgia and I were thinking quite a lot of each other. I had never really proposed to her yet but I told her, I said, "Georgia, I tell you what I'm going to do. I'll chuck the dice with you to see if you will marry me."

"How?" she asked.

"Just roll it out. If I beat your number we'll get married."

She held the dice in her hand and threw it on the flat top of the stump. It rolled over and over, came up a five spot.

"Oh, no," I moaned.

"What's the matter? What's the matter?"

"Well," I said, "there's only six spots on a dice. I have one chance out of six to beat you."

"Throw it."

I did and got a six. The way I hollered you could have heard it up to the moon.

"Now you will marry me!"

"When?" is all she said. And that was that, we were married on a throw of the dice.

Georgia and I got along well but of course little differences were bound to show up. For instance, a Children's Day came up out on the flat. It was a big church dinner and all the inlaws and outlaws got together for a feed and a chance to top the other fellow.

We had a little farm about three miles from town and I was working hay when Georgia came and asked if we could go to Children's Day. I had to get the hay up. I was working seven days a week and to save time I would mow one evening, late as I could, and the next night I would rake it. That way I could get my hay cut, raked and ready to haul. I was hauling Sunday, Children's Day.

Georgia came out and I told her, "Now I am perfectly willing to take you and the girls but I have work to get done here. What if it starts raining?"

We had two girls by then and Georgia was concerned that we go to the church picnic as a family. She was worried about what people would say.

"I don't give a damn what they say," I told her. "I have to get this hay to the barn."

"Chuck the dice, George Kennedy," she told me and I brought it out of my pocket. "Let's see whether you go or not."

I won and I asked if she and the girls would accept a ride. I was willing to stop long enough to run them to the church.

"Well," Georgia said, "could you use some help? What if I drove team — you could pitch hay on the wagon. That way you don't have to jump on and off."

It turned out the kids rode the team, Georgia drove and I pitched. We hauled hay straight through the day.

For years that dice was the way we settled arguments. After Georgia died there wasn't much use keeping the dice. The corners were rounded and about half the spots were gone. I gave it to a new married couple I know. I told them, "You take this dice. Any little argument starts, chuck the dice, high man wins."

My sister Carrie never did a lick, all she wanted to do was sit around and crochet and embroider. Me, well Daddy only let me go two years of school before going to work full time.

The two years I had were at the schoolhouse down from Elgin, Oregon. Cougars were so thick around there that Daddy used to drive over the hill and watch me coming or going. I remember him yet standing up above me with a rifle in his hands, leaning against the wagon. And I was about as scared as a human being can be. I heard hundreds of cougars scream. Believe me, if they are close when they scream it just makes the hair jump right out of the back of your neck. I saw them close beside the trail and imagined them on every overhanging limb but they knew Daddy would kill them. They left me alone.

When I was eight years old Daddy pulled me out of school and had me work full time. Daddy had been a machinist back in Missouri and our house was right next door to his shop. From the time I was eight years old he had me working. After all my sister wouldn't and Daddy needed help, even if I wasn't a boy.

I pumped the bellows and Daddy stood at the forge shaping horseshoes. He was a big, muscular man and would work with sweat pouring off him from sunrise until way after dark. Mother would call dinner was ready and that is when we would stop. I was there every minute and being so close I learned. I can use an anvil and shoe a horse better than most men.

Daddy and I were working one day when a drummer came in to the shop pushing an automobile. I had heard of them but this was the first I laid eyes on. He asked if Daddy could fix it and make it run.

"Sure thing," Daddy told him but the truth of the matter was that Father had never seen an automobile. The drummer went on up to Wallowa County by horse-drawn stage. Daddy did the mechanic work by trial and error and if we pushed that car up the hill once, we must have pushed it a hundred times. I think Daddy just enjoyed steering.

When the drummer came back his Model T Ford was running better than it ever had. Our blacksmith shop in the years that followed became more of a garage and I was a grease monkey.

To tell the truth I can do most anything. I can set a ratchet and saw off a board with anyone. I worked in the sawmill when I was ten.

Late the fall of 1908 we were living in Island City. There came a knock on the door and I opened it to a young man. He was quite handsome, about my age.

"Ma'am, my name is Alfred Fuller and my folks and I are traveling through and would like to find a spot where we can rest the horses for a few days. Do you know of a place?"

I told him I was sure they could put up in the pasture but I had to check with Daddy. Daddy said they could.

The Fuller family was there for three days and Alfred and I became acquainted with each other. We went for walks and talked. Then he was gone.

He wrote a letter to me from Sherman County where his folks settled and in it he said he had a job. But the best news was that he wanted to come visit and spend Christmas with me. I was so excited.

Just before Christmas Alfred came in on the train. He walked to our house carrying his suitcase and when I opened the door he looked even better than the first time. Alfred was going to stay at the hotel but when he started to leave Mother stopped him.

"I have extra beds and one is made up for you. Stay here," she said.

Before Alfred left for his job in Sherman County he asked me to marry him. Of course I said yes. On the 27th of June 1909 we were married.

Alfred went to work at a potato packing shed in Island City and I went to keeping house in La Grande. As a newlywed I wanted to do things right and one day I decided to take a nice hot lunch to Alfred. We had bought a Franklin automobile, I had never driven before but decided to drive that day. After all I wasn't going to learn any younger.

I got everything ready and didn't have a lick of trouble until I got to Island City. There they were putting in the first electrical line and I don't know — maybe I was watching them. At any rate I ran off the road, through a little ditch and straddled one of their power poles lying on the ground. I was high-centered and didn't know how to find reverse.

The potato shed crew heard all the commotion and came to investigate. Alfred was among them.

"Oh my God," he said, "how in the world did you get all the way out here without hitting anything and then end up straddling a pole?"

The men had to lift the Franklin off the pole. They turned me around and headed me for town. And when I got home I discovered that Alfred's hot lunch was still on the seat beside me; I had forgotten.

We arrived in eastern Oregon fall of the year, harvest time. We were low on money and supplies so we swung off the Oregon Trail and my father and six brothers looked for work. They caught on at a ranch out of Drewsey hauling hay and we ended up wintering there. Dad fed cattle and all of us children went to school.

Come spring we were back on the road. In The Dalles a spotter got hold of Dad, claiming he knew of good land available to homestead. He offered to show us where.

''The land won't cost you a cent,'' the spotter promised. ''All you have to do is file and live there. Of course, there is the small matter of my commission. But you have to remember that is the only cost to owning your own land.''

The deal sounded too good for Father to pass. The spotter took us out, him on a nice saddle horse and us in the wagon, to our new home. It was a place called Happy Ridge. There was scrub oak and some pine — spotty. We filed on a natural meadow and planted it to grain, raised cattle, chickens, pigs.

We were the first white people to settle on that tract of land and of course when we got there we didn't have a house. Father, Mother, six brothers and me — we lived in a tent and cooked outdoors.

Father bought rough lumber from a sawmill and we built a two-story, twenty-four by sixteen-foot house. The cracks were batted. Upstairs was a sleeping loft for the boys. Downstairs was the living room which doubled as my bedroom, the kitchen, dining room and the parents' little bedroom. These rooms had wallpaper covering over the pine lumber.

All the while I was growing we always would lay in a stock of wild berries before winter. On Happy Ridge you took anything free; it was a tough place to make a living. We led saddle horses on the side of Mt. Hood to pick huckleberries. There were oodles of huckleberries and when we filled two five-gallon oil cans we tied them on the saddle and led the horses.

When I was old enough to get out of the house and work I went to the Rondeau place as cook. They had a nice farm and one of the men working for them became my husband, Harry Lewis. Originally he had come from Nebraska headed for the gold diggings in Alaska. He hopped a ride on a sheep train and got as far as Portland before he was stranded. He didn't have enough money to get to Alaska but he used what he had to buy a run-down horse.

Harry started backtracking for Nebraska but the nag gave out and he abandoned it near Mosier. He heard of work on the flatland above the Columbia and the first farm he tried in Tygh Ridge was Rondeau's.

That is how I met Harry Lewis and in 1907, April 24th, we were married.

At first we rented land; we had some good years, but the bad ate it up. In the late '20s we pulled together enough to buy our first place on Smock Prairie. It was small but it was our own.

"We're not doing anything but staying even," Harry told me one evening. "The government is loaning money to farmers, I think we should borrow and buy milk cows. We can sell cream for a good price and skim milk can go to pigs. I say we should try it."

Whatever Harry wanted to do was all right with me, he was boss. The market was high at that point in time. Cows were going for no less than a hundred dollars and when we got our federal land bank loan Harry paid up to $135 a head for fourteen milk cows.

Our children helped with the chores and for the first time it looked as if our family would not be poor. Then the depression hit. It knocked our feet right out from under us and the cows — nobody wanted cows. Good, fat steers, ready for market, brought only ten dollars — if you found a buyer.

We held on by the skin of our teeth for a few years but then lost the milk cows and lost the place on Smock Prairie. We went back to renting land, Harry and the boys worked out. Harry was a good man in harvest, he had experience running steam engines and once the automobile became popular he studied and could do about anything that needed to be done mechanically to a Model A.

For a few years we lived on Juniper Flat. Harry was a ditch walker and the last two children, the twins, were born there. Then we moved on down in the valley to Sandy. We grew old there and when Harry was 77 he had a stroke that part way paralyzed one side of his body. He was crippled but lived ten more years.

I don't remember Harry after he was stricken. When I think about him, and I think about him all the time, I remember him at the dances. Down to Wamic, Tygh Valley, Dufur — playing his fiddle and dancing, kicking up his heels to "Turkey in the Straw."

It is a pity, I suppose, but we all have to get old. All I wish is that it was somehow easier.

We did a lot over the years to improve the homestead at Big Butte. Dad built a barn and then when we could afford it he built a house and tore down the homestead cabin.

The closest town to our place was Grangeville and every few weeks we went in. Every time we had to pass "our last camping spot" as my sisters Nanny and Ella called it. It was in a little dip on upper Lawyer Creek and had been the last campsite on our wagon trip west. After that night we were to Killmar's, our destination.

There was never a time we passed the spot that Nanny and Ella would not call attention to the fact. And usually reminiscences followed.

"Remember that doll we left in Montpelier, just after we crossed into Idaho?" one of them would always say. Since I was too young to remember much of what went on they would tell me the story. This went on hundreds — no, thousands of times.

According to the story, by the time we had reached the Idaho border our horses were in rough shape and Dad decided to leave one wagon. That night Mother went through and sorted everything. She kept very little of the wagon's contents. In the morning we pulled away leaving the wagon on the outskirts of Montpelier. Somehow my sisters' doll was left behind; we didn't aim to leave it.

My sisters talked and talked about that doll and seventy-five years after we made the wagon trip they talked me into going back to Montpelier and looking for our wagon. I thought it was funny, they really wanted to go.

We drove to Montpelier in a car and looked around. It had changed — the valley was the same, long and narrow, but the town had more people than I remembered. We drove back streets and my sisters stopped and looked inside rundown garages. The wagon was not to be found and after looking for hours we drove on following the old trail.

That night in the motel room Nanny and Ella sat on the bed discussing where the doll might be. They thought our wagon was still in Montpelier somewhere, it was just that we hadn't found it.

An uncle of ours, Uncle Scott, lived back in the Blue Mountains of Oregon at Hidaway Hot Springs. When I was sixteen I left my father and brothers and came to Pendleton. Uncle Scott picked me up at the train station and I started cooking at Hidaway.

Still, I found time to do what I liked best — ride horses. I ate, slept, breathed horses and discovered that none could buck me. That was the fun part. I rode everything.

My first real competition was in La Grande. A man offered me a hundred dollars if I would crawl on a bucking horse and I did, riding the worst cayuse he had.

I never competed unless there was a guarantee, up front, and that hundred dollars I got in La Grande was the least I ever took. I rode in Cheyenne and won the first Calgary Stampede — in the five-day show I brought home $1,000 and first place. Bertha Blanchett took second and Tillie Baldwin was third. That was the most money I ever made at one show.

I received top billing everywhere I went; I autographed my picture; fliers read "Champion Ladies Bronc Rider — Blanche McGaughey."

What set me apart from the other girls who rode bucking horses was that I knew how to handle myself and I was good-looking. I wore long black hair braided down to my waist and any one of three suits. The skirts were made of tanned sheepskin; I had a red one, a brown and a natural tan. The hat was always black and I wore blouses with a bit of color.

I didn't jazz around at night, I behaved myself. I didn't drink but I did like to dance, although I refrained while competing. I treated myself like an athlete.

At the Pendleton Round-Up of 1912 I came to prove what I could do. Picture an Indian summer afternoon, not an empty seat in the house, a solid mass of people dressed in bright colors and cowboy hats. They cheer and the band begins to play.

I came out on a horse called Battling Nelson and rode him to a standstill. From my point of view it was only a fair ride but the crowd cheered and whistled, they enjoyed the heck out of it.

The bucking horse I rode for the silver cup and title of Cowgirl Bucking Championship of the Northwest was a mean little sidewinder named Stubtoe. He was awkward when he bucked and got his name due to the fact that he stumbled a lot unless you knew enough to hold his head up.

A couple of cowboys brought Stubtoe into the arena, one eared him down while the other tied on the blindfold. The saddle was being cinched when I made my appearance. The crowd cheered and I waved.

As I started to climb aboard, Stubtoe shied and the cowboy on the ears brought him down to his knees. I accepted a hand up and all around the excitement built to a roar in my ears.

"Turn him loose," I commanded, nodding in the direction of the blindfold man. He stepped away and so did the fellow on ears.

Stubtoe stood there for a short second until he realized I was on his back, then he came unglued. Now, I, I can stick on the back of a horse like a fly. Stubtoe found that out. I finished raking, both hands in the air. When Stubtoe stopped I slid to the ground and the applause was thunderous.

I left my mark when I rode Stubtoe to a standstill. I was a celebrity and because of it a few of the other lady riders were jealous. I was attractive, had money, nice clothes, admirers — they held that against me.

The worst it got was during a relay race at the Pendleton Round-Up. One green-eyed girl on the third leg of the race quartered her horse into mine. We were going full speed and I know it was done on purpose. The force of the butt drove my horse, which was on the inside, against the rail. I knew my leg hit pretty hard but there was no pain, only the speed of the horse. We outran everyone in the field and when I went to pull up, my catcher was yelling at the top of his lungs, "Goddamit, Goddamit, you won, you won the race!"

"Yes," I told him, "I did, but I also broke my leg."

Well, he got excited, jumping around and screaming, "Goddamit, someone do something. She's broke her leg."

By then a few of the cowboys were coming over from inside the arena. I was so disgusted with the entire outfit that I lifted my leg over and jumped to the ground. Pain shot clear to my head, I must have gone white as a sheet because the catcher starts yelling again, "Goddamit, someone catch her."

I wasn't about to pass out, I walked from the race track to where the automobiles were parked. All I had to lean on was Bertha Blanchett. Out in the parking lot the doctor caught up with us, I sat down and told him to go ahead and cut my boot off. He said no he couldn't do that, my boot was too pretty. So he pulled it off and it hurt like you know what.

After I got over the broken leg another rider, John Spain, and myself put on what was called the Little Pendleton Round-Up. What we did was travel around the Northwest, John riding the bucking horse and bulldogging the steer we brought along. I did the same. We were working for the Round-Up getting them publicity.

The easy part of the job was the money, a hundred a week plus if someone brought in a horse we could bet on the side. The hard part was that the bulldogging steer got to be a pet. We called him Whitey.

Well, down in Astoria it had been raining for a solid week and I had to throw Whitey in the mud. John came out as my hazer and we ran Whitey between us. I leaned over and dropped on Whitey; and when I went to get footing I couldn't, my feet just slid and slid. After Whitey slowed I tried to force his head over and flip him on his back. We stood there toe to toe in the middle of the arena, him never moving anything except his head and me pulling this way and that, slipping each time that I did. I fell down in the mud and got back up. There was just no way I was going to throw Whitey this time. I turned to the stands and said, ''Gentlemen, I am sorry but tonight I cannot throw this steer.'' I ended up getting a bigger hand than if I would have thrown him.

After the Little Pendleton Round-Up I got on with the Hundred-and-One outfit. They were a traveling cowboy show and over the course of the year we worked our way from Portland to New York City. I rode bucking broncs in Madison Square Garden for a week and was the star. There were posters that read, ''Ladies Only Bucking Horse Rider in the World.'' To make things tougher I rode slick, pride wouldn't let me tie the stirrups no matter how mean the horse. And people brought in some mean horses.

With the Hundred-and-One I got a hundred a week each and every week. It was the first steady job I had but after the tour was over I wasn't any farther ahead. I liked to buy nice things and I was always an easy mark. Everyone in the show borrowed money from me, few ever paid it back.

I went on my own, riding rodeos here and there — always with an up-front guarantee. I suppose I figured it would go on forever.

September 1914 came and I took the train to The Dalles. They were having a show and I was doing bronc riding and bulldogging.

It was at that show that I met Ted Sammis. He was a farmer and on the rodeo committee. We talked and enjoyed each other's company. A few months later I was coming through The Dalles on my way to Hollywood to make a movie when Ted met me at the railroad station and asked me to marry him. After that I was content to settle down and clean house. Ted asked me if I still didn't want to ride bucking horses or bulldog and I told him no, and never again rode in competition.

Instead I became the best cook in the county, people all said that. The few times I did catch myself in the saddle were usually during parades.

I was in my mid-eighties when I took what I figure was my final ride. It was at a family get-together. Of course the kids congregated around the barn where the horses were. I went down just to kind of nose around and see what they were doing. Five of the kids were on horses and as soon as I showed my face they wanted to see me ride.

"Show us how you rode Snake."

"Show us how you rode Scar Leg at Pendleton."

They had heard all the stories about me and I wasn't going to have a little thing like age hold me back.

"Well, one of you will have to get down and give me a horse," I told them and one got down. He had to hold the horse for me but I got on by myself — foot in the stirrup and pulled. It felt good to be sitting there, real natural. I thought about my red sheepskin dress, the crowd and waving my black hat to them. They roared and cheered.

"Aunt Blanche, get down off that horse right now. You could hurt yourself," a niece hollered at me from the house.

"Fat chance of that happening," I yelled back and the kids and I rode several miles before we turned around. We talked about the Hundred-and-One, the money in Calgary and winning the bronc busting title at Pendleton. Those kids shared my final ride.

While I lived with the Rineharts on their farm outside Yamhill, Oregon, I had an accident. Some wild horses we had gathered jammed, I was between them. I was mounted on a saddle horse and when they squeezed together they crushed my leg. The doctors took it off.

After that, I didn't know if any man would want me but Bert said it didn't matter. Bert Dexter was my sweetheart since I was a girl and we married in front of Rineharts' great stone fireplace.

For several years we traveled, working here and there, and then came back and took over Rineharts' farm. We raised prunes until the market went bad and we went broke. Bert decided we should start over in eastern Oregon and he found a small farm for sale near Umatilla.

The year was 1914 and by then we had five children. Bert moved all our household things with a wagon and team, taking the two youngest boys with him. Then he came back for the rest of us in a Model T.

After we moved into the place at Umatilla we parked the wagon behind the barn and it eventually rotted away. The team died of old age. As for the Model T, we drove that several years then parked it at the fence corner nearest the house.

It sat there out in the weather for maybe five or six more years before a man named Goebel from Wallowa County came by and offered us $20. Bert sold it as fast as he could, thinking we were getting the deal. But as it turned out Goebel drove that Model T back and forth to Kansas twice and never had a bit of trouble.

That just goes to show.

It took us six months to come from Goodland, Kansas, to Oregon because we had to stop all the time so the men could work and earn money. We cut off the Oregon Trail and came across the desert through Bend. Father and his brother found work there in hay harvest but never made more than a dollar a day for the worst kind of work.

Our goal was the Willamette Valley but when we topped the Cascades it looked like we had finally been stopped just a few miles short. There was a tollgate set up at Soda Springs and a man was there to collect. We didn't have the money to pay and Mother was afraid he would make us turn around and go back. All the money we could muster was a dollar and a half.

"If you have come this far," said the old fellow at the tollgate, "and only have a buck and a half, I'll be damned if I am the man to take it. Go ahead, go on. I'll charge the next man who can afford it twice. Good luck to you."

On the west side of the mountains we stopped near the town of Foster. We lived from pillar to post until a family was good enough to take us in. They let us stay in a log cabin and Dad worked for them in the field.

While I was growing up we had a neighbor boy named Wayne Menear and I thought quite a lot of him. I was nineteen and Wayne was four years older when we were married. He worked in the woods cutting timber and we made our home close to wherever he worked, sometimes that meant camping.

Wayne was always the happiest when out in the woods. He loved trees and once our son Virgil was old enough to go with him Wayne took him into the woods. Virgil cut his eyeteeth on a cross-cut saw.

Wayne and Virgil were a team and it went on that way until the day Virgil came running into the house. He was early. I met him in the kitchen.

"It's Dad, real bad, Mom," he said and I knew there had been an accident. "He isn't dead yet.

"We were cutting a big pine, almost through, and the wind caught the top. Dad tried to run but didn't make it."

They had Wayne in the hospital at Sweet Home and a day later we took him to Good Samaritan in Portland. Doctors there didn't give him much of a chance; they put two steel plates in his head and ever after he had a bit of paralysis on the right side. Under the circumstances a little paralysis was something we could learn to live with.

Wayne never went back to work in the woods but he spent plenty of time there. We hunted and fished and I remember him telling me while we were waiting for a fish to bite that the days he had a cross-cut saw in his hands were the best days of his life. He learned to adapt, I guess we all have to, and even with his paralysis he was the best shot around. He won every turkey shoot he ever entered, shot a .32 long-barrel, and I saw him drive a nail in a tree at a hundred yards — never miss.

All my life I got along with horses, we was like bread and butter, and the best team I ever had was a mare and a gelding named Topsy and Joe. They were Percheron, one just as good as the other. I could hitch them to an even doubletree and they would hold it steady. They got down easy together and held right there until the sun would set and longer if I wanted them to.

One time over in Elgin there was a fellow putting on an exhibition with a team of horses. He was pulling a one-ton rock on a sled and as a sideline he offered to wager that there was not a horse alive that could pull the rock by himself. A friend of mine was there and when he heard this fellow make the wager he stood up and said, "By God, George Craig has a horse that could move the world if he was hitched to it. If he is in town I have $500 that says he can move your rock."

Well, it just so happened that I was in town and I had brought Topsy with me. When my friend found me I told him that moving a ton rock on bare ground was going to be tough. He said he already had his money down and that he would lose it unless I gave her a try. I was game and so was Topsy.

Rules was that I had three attempts to move the sled and it had to go ten feet. I hitched up Topsy and told her to get down on it. She got down to where her belly was maybe six inches off the ground and just wiggled the sled the least little bit. Whoa, I told her. She was twisted at an angle and I had her get over.

The fellow who owned the rock sled said, "That's one pull." I ignored him and straightened out Topsy. Topsy was a dark chocolate brown, fifteen hundred pounds and as fine a horse as ever lived. If Topsy couldn't make the pull then it could not be pulled. I slapped her one on the butt and told her, by God, to get down. She went to her belly with all four feet spitting dirt. The sled started moving and I didn't stop until we were well past the line. We needed ten feet and made twelve.

My friend was so happy that he offered to give me the full five hundred that he won. I told him no, but I did take half of it and then we went to the saloon and had a few drinks. Before the night was over we got ourselves pretty well lit and when I woke the next morning I still had change in my pocket.

I always had the best horses around because that was my job — I used them for logging. There wasn't no damn stick in the woods that I couldn't haul and I was all over the Blues and Wallowas.

There was one tree back in the Blues that was too big for anyone else to haul, it was left until I cut it down. The tree was a Ponderosa, better than six feet at the stump and eighty or ninety feet tall. I told a friend of mine that I was going to bring the butt log out and he said, "By God, if you are loading that today then I have to come and watch."

He rode with me and when we got to the log I deadheaded the wagon with a chain to a tree and put small logs angled up from the ground to the wagon. Topsy and Joe I put to work. They took hold of the big log; they got down and stayed there for more than a minute; then the log started moving. We loaded in nothing flat and on the way back to the mill in Summerville my friend rode on the log like he was marshal of a parade.

I logged for better than fifty years and in all that time there was only once I ever really hurt myself. That day I was bringing out another big load. Usually I chain a load down but for some reason this day I did not. The road was steep, going downhill, and I had the brake rope across my legs and was sitting on it.

A kid was driving a second load and was right behind when we started down the section where the road was really rough. In fact, on that part of the grade we had made a second road right beside the first and it was just after I entered the new section that my front wheel hit a chuckhole and dropped out of sight. One of the logs I had on rolled. It happened fast. The log caught the end of the brake rope and flipped me off the seat and onto the ground. I landed and then the log came over my legs, rolled back. The log ended up settling against the wheels of the wagon, pinning the brake rope. I knew my legs were broke, and they were — both below the knee.

The young feller that was following seen the accident happen. He was at the top of the grade. My wagon was blocking the new road. I was laying in the middle of the old road. I looked up and the kid jumped off his wagon to come and help. He threw the reins down and as soon as he did that his team started running.

Now I was in one hell of a fix, laying there in the road without a chance of moving and the loaded wagon barreling down on me. I figured it would run right over the top but the horses went for the new road and stayed with it. They ran right in to the back of my wagon and the tongue stuck into a log. When they hit, the horses went down and then were a little goofy in the head.

The wagon tongue was stuck in the log tight as could be, there was no way to free it and so once I was out from under the logs I told the young fellow to unhitch my team and put me on Topsy. I figured on riding. He did what he was told, got me on her back and then went to unhitch his own team. Hell, at that point I had no strength left and when the kid turned his back I fell off Topsy. God, talk about hurt — I hurt all over. Both legs were broke, my head hurt, my back hurt . . . .

The kid got me up on Topsy again and so I wouldn't fall a second time I had him tie my two broken legs together under the horse and take a wrap around my body and the hames. There was no way I could fall but every little move Topsy made hurt like a knife shoved in my side. It was eight miles in to Summerville and I thought I was going to die before I got there. I didn't.

That accident was the only time in my life that I was every really hurt bad, although when I was seventy years old I took a hell of a chance and probably should have ended up in some damn hospital. That all came about because of an uncle of mine lived in Seattle.

He ran across a man that owned a horse that he said could not be rode. My uncle said, "Oh, yes he can be rode and I know the man that can do it. He lives in Oregon." My uncle was talking about me. He called on the phone and told me to come to Seattle, he had money on the line.

I carried my saddle because I was used to riding it and took the train to Seattle. When I got there and saw the horse they were talking about I had some reservations. He was a big reddish brown, went every bit of twelve hundred pounds and his disposition was on the short side of mean.

I had along a pair of spurs that I wired so they could not roll. I put them on and before we could saddle the big red we had to ear him down. I climbed up and didn't ride like any seventy-year-old man. I dug those spurs in just as tight as I could get them — let that big red go on about his business. He jumped in the air and tried to come over backwards. I don't know how he done it, but he did. By God, I stayed with him. I socked those spurs in his ribs, he couldn't budge me. Around and 'round and 'round, I rode that son of a bitch to a standstill and when he was done bucking I slid off him like I was some kid.

My uncle wanted to give me all the money; I took only half. I earned every bit of it, too, and it was a week before the soreness wore off enough so I could get out of bed and go home.

That week and the time I came down with the flu in 1918 was really the only times I ever have been confined to bed. I worked every other day of my life. We would log six days a week, the men laying off on Sunday, and I would use the time to repair machinery. I never even celebrated the Fourth of July.

My wife used to say that we would work hard while we were young so that when we were old we would have money and everything would be all right. But she died a few years back and I found out that an old man by himself is better off with no money at all.

I don't mind the rest home. Why not too long ago a girl came in here and claimed she wanted to marry me. I said, "Jesus Christ, you don't want me, I can't do no one nothing."

Hell, if I had life to do over again I would have a good time while I was young. When you get old you can't, you feel sick. I don't feel good no more. I get nervous and my stomach goes on the fritz unless I get my regular sling before every meal. I drink Old Rocking Chair. The nurses go down and buy it for me but I have to give them the money. A fifth will last a week. I get up at six in the morning for a sling before breakfast and have the same before dinner and supper.

I have to take a sling so I can eat. The doctor told me to do it. He said that was all that was keeping me alive. I got my swaller broke loose from my dyphram and the doctor told me that when that gets to bothering me to have a sling. He doesn't want me to drink until I'm drunk, just until the hurting stops.

All my life I've smoked Prince Albert in a corn cob pipe and drank a little whiskey on occasions but since I came to this rest home I take slings as medicine. At first it was God-awful bitter. I told the nurse that she was either putting in too much whiskey or not enough water. Now they add a half a spoon of sugar and it's just right.

A new nurse came in one time and I told her I wanted a sling. She asked what I was talking about and I told her I was talking about a whiskey sling.

"I'm not about to let you drink no whiskey," she told me. I explained how I got a sling with every meal. She called me a liar. Another old feller was sitting beside me and he said, "Yes, Ma'am, George gets a sling every meal." "I bet you do, too," the nurse said to him and he told her that once every so often he drank some whiskey. "Well, you ain't a goin' to get any whiskey," she told us.

About that time the regular nurse comes in and I'm all humped up in a chair. I won't eat, supper is gettin' cold in front of me. "What's wrong?" the nurse asks me and so I tell her how I didn't get my sling. "Well, I'll take care of that," she said and took off to go find the new nurse. And it wasn't more than five minutes until that new nurse was in there with my sling.

I could take a sling every five minutes if I wanted to. My doctor told me I could. I have a good doctor, been going to him for twenty years, and he told them I should take a sling and if that didn't cure me I should take another.

My back is busted up pretty bad now and I've got arthritis in my fingers. They got crooked a few years back and hurt all the time but they are straightening out and don't hurt much now.

Up until a week or so ago I was doing all right. Now if I get up too quick I get dizzy and I'll pitch over on my head. I get nervous quite a bit and when I do a nurse will come in and say, "Come on, George, time for your sling."

A few years back, when I was 94, the doctor told me I wasn't going to make it. You know my swaller is separated from my dyphram. He said I should get rid of my stuff and so I give the kids all they wanted and sold the rest. I got three thousand bucks.

Oh hell, I know I ain't a gonna live forever. I've had a good life and I know I have to die. But damn, if I can last until the 18th day of October in 1983 I will be a hundred. And I would like to be able to brag it around that I was a hundred.

The Return

I live in a cabin on the Deschutes River, spend my time catching German brown and steelhead. The fish are the reason I get up every morning, they bring challenge to the day.

Fishing may be my passion but a man cannot live on fish alone. Since I get no pension I sell firewood. I don't need to have two good legs to cut firewood. Besides, that gives me an excuse to be out in the woods. The rest of the time I fish.

Friends, acquaintances I meet along the river in the fog and in rain are true fishermen — diehards. There is one old fellow, about my age, we call No Good. We named him that because whenever you ask him how is he doing he answers, "No good." But one look in his creel — perpetually packed with fish.

Early one June morning in 1923 No Good and I cross paths. In the conversation that follows No Good says, "You going to the doings? Didn't you tell me that you came out over the Oregon Trail? Well, the President of the United States is going to dedicate it. You thought about going? It's being held up to Meacham, summit of the Blue Mountains."

"When did you say this is going to happen?" I question.

"Next week. President Warren G. Harding is coming in on the train to speak. Should be quite the crowd there."

In the back of my mind I know I am going, and when the following week rolls around I am in my automobile heading to Meacham.

This is my first return to the Blue Mountains since our wagon trip west. Meacham, Emigrant Springs. More than names of places to me, they are emotions and memories of burying Willie so many years ago. For us the summit of the Blues had been misery that I had not wanted to face until now.

Pendleton is in no way familiar. It seems civilized and citified. Coming up the grade east of town I look back and Pendleton becomes a spot down in the canyon. Ahead, the road twists and winds going straight up. I wonder how we ever came down in a wagon. Twice my rig boils over and I hike to water buckets conveniently placed along the roadway. The motorist has life easy.

Above the bald west face near timberline, a road crew is working, putting finishing touches on the last link of the east-west highway. It will be dedicated to replace the Oregon Trail and one of the fellows tells me they're going to have it in A-1 condition for the "Old Man." And I take it to mean the President.

At Emigrant Springs I pull off and park. The springs and the spot where we had camped is about a half mile south of the road. I hike through lodgepole thickets, come to a small meadow and find what I think is the place. I can't be a hundred percent sure, trees have grown and the meadow has shrunk.

Walking in the same direction I once walked I locate a depression, three feet by five feet. Willie's grave. Buttercups, little white flowers and Indian paintbrush grow like a carpet. The log we had placed as protection has rotted to nothing. There is not even a trace remaining.

I stand there thinking back to a time long ago, a day where I had all life ahead of me. Willie's had just ended. Oh, what he missed!

I picture Willie a ten-year-old boy, he never got older. Ten years, freckles and hand-me-down trousers that he hadn't grown into — that's Willie. I see him walking along, Yellow at his side.

"Why," I ask out loud, "couldn't Willie have lived?"

From the familiar scab rock with the unchanging dwarf pine I watch the sun go behind the shadow of the Cascades and am left wondering if the sunsets always run red on top of the Blues.

The following day I drive to Meacham and a good-sized gathering of people have taken residency on the meadow. I drive past looking for a camp spot off by myself.

In the middle of the meadow wanders a little creek. I find a spot near the bank and park my car. I should unpack, set up camp, but instead I put together my bamboo fly rod and go fishing.

Before I start fishing I lie down on the bank and peer into the water. It gives me an idea on what the fish are feeding.

I see a reflection in the water of an old man, thin face and stubble growth of two weeks. A scar across the right eye makes it droop. I smile. The face smiles back. And then I see a trout, a whopping big trout swimming without a care in the world. I ease back and drop an imitation of a black nymph on the water. A few minutes pass and I work the fly.

Bam! He takes it. Line goes out and I have to run along the bank until my fish finally tires. I lift him from the water and cook him for dinner over the fire.

The next afternoon a number of Indians arrive. They ride single file and a pack string brings up the rear. They camp not far from me, on the opposite side of the stream, and squaws do all the work. They erect tepees, gather wood and start fires. The bucks go hunting and return with a cow elk. They eat.

The day of the celebration everyone is awake early. Families parade past on their way to the railroad station. They want to catch the first glimpse of President Harding. The men wear hats, coats and ties and the women sport store-bought dresses. I shave, put on my clean shirt and follow the procession.

The smell of bacon hangs low over the meadow when far off the sound of a whistle is heard. Indians come running.

I stand beside the track as the President comes past. He waves from the observation deck. The train stops and a man on a horse slides to a halt beside the President's car.

"Mr. President and Mrs. Harding, we welcome you to the wide open spaces, from the pines to the prairies, this land is yours. Welcome."

After the cowboy's one-way exchange a group of civic leaders from La Grande and Pendleton rush in and shake the hand of a living, breathing President. They retire inside his private car and it is not until noon that any of us see movement.

President and Mrs. Harding step forth as if they are on a date. She wears a simple, not too expensive-looking dress. And the President is decked in a plain straw hat, blue coat, green tie and light-striped trousers. He wears no vest but on his lapel is a badge which reads, "President Harding." Hell, everyone knows who he is.

A stagecoach of the Concord variety takes the Hardings across the meadow to where a reviewing stand is located. The crowd follows on foot and as I get there a band dressed in coveralls strikes a march. The President takes his chair and the festivities begin. Looking over the sea of people different groups can be identified. There are clusters of cowboys in chaps and hats, city folks and whiskered pioneers who had seen the Oregon Trail in its heyday. Topping the summit then, the only cheers had been their own.

At the far end of the meadow a line of covered wagons come into view. They skirt the edge of the timber and come straight toward the reviewing stand. Girls and women in calico sit on the wagon seats while men walk alongside leading the teams. The crowd cheers as the symbolic last wagon train passes Presidential review.

"Come up here with me, you, and you," the President calls, pointing to the wagon train. An old man who says his name is Charles Becker shakes hands with the President. He says he made an oxen crossing and the President pumps his hand as if he is the one honored. The other guest invited on the review stand is a boy, roughly dressed with a red handkerchief around his neck and a tall plug hat on his head. The President whispers something in his ear meant only for him and then lifts the lad back to the ground. The boy disappears in the crowd.

The wagon train drives from sight and a mounted guard takes its place. Silver trappings on saddles and bridles reflect in the sun. The next entry is the delegation of Indians, bucks mounted and the squaws and children walking. They shuffle past, refusing to look at the white chief.

The program finally gets to speeches and the President reads a typewritten story about Marcus Whitman leading the first wagon west. And then the President has a surprise. He proclaims Meacham the Capitol of the United States. For one day Meacham is something; a footnote in history.

After this I expect to hear the dedication but instead it is announced that the official ceremony to dedicate the Oregon Trail will be held three miles away at Emigrant Springs.

I know where Emigrant Springs is and start walking. A Model T stops beside me.

"Want a ride? If you're walking to the dedication you're going to miss it."

The driver is an old man and as I open the door and crawl in my attention is drawn to his white beard which flows inside his top coat. The old man begins the conversation.

"I come all the way from California for this dedication. I wouldn't have missed it."

"Did you come over the trail?" I ask, knowing in my mind he did.

"Sure did, and not once but several times. A fellow showed me how to make money leading wagon trains west."

"What was that fellow's name?" I ask, curious.

"Well," the old man said, "I don't remember hearing his God-given name. He was always plain 'Cal' and as he used to say, 'Named that in due respect to the great state of California'."

"What happened to him? Do you know where Cal is now?"

"Yes, I do. Cal is dead and buried. He returned to the Sacramento Valley after being back east, rode a mustang and trailed a pack mule. Came straight to my place and though he was in rough shape he was happy. Winter came and he died in his sleep. Said he always figured to die violently but no, he died in his sleep."

To me there is only one reason to be at Meacham and that is for the dedication at Emigrant Springs. Besides the old man and me there is only a handful of others who have bothered to come.

The President reads a short address about the westward migration and how important the Oregon Trail has been. He finishes by saying:

"The Oregon Trail lives on . . . . in the eyes of time we have changed, improved. No longer do we rely on the team and wagon. We have the automobile . . . . I hereby dedicate the Oregon Trail. May it long be remembered. And I hereby open the Oregon Trail highway. A benefit to all mankind."

Once the President leaves everyone starts back toward his automobile. The old man asks if I want a ride. I tell him no.

They are gone and I stand alone. To me the Oregon Trail broke my heart, but it made a man of me. The Oregon Trail — Willie is gone, Mother and Pa passed away after a full life, and now to learn Cal had done the same. At least he died in California.

I am the holdover, the end of an era. I walk down the old wagon road, looking at what remains. There is no fresh sign in the trail; flowers and grass grow in a mask. And in between ruts, where the ground is a little softer, there are trees.

We wish to thank all the pioneers and their families who shared with us so that we could share with you.

The Authors

Historical Notes

THE OREGON TRAIL

Credit for discovering the route which became the Old Oregon Trail is generally given to Wilson Price Hunt's Expedition of 1810–1812. His party blazed a trail from Snake River to the mouth of the Columbia.

In 1812 Robert Stuart and six companions left Astoria on the Columbia heading overland to New York. They followed in Hunt's tracks and went on to discover South Pass and the trail which followed the Sweetwater and Platte rivers.

By the late 1830s missionaries were playing a major role in developing the Oregon Trail. The names are many but include Marcus and Narcissa Whitman, Henry and Eliza Spalding and Jason and Daniel Lee.

Spring of 1841 witnessed the departure from Independence, Missouri, of a small wagon train led by John Bidwell. The party split at Soda Spring, half going to California and the remainder to Oregon. The following year the real march west began with an official trail expedition led by John C. Fremont and the Elijah White wagon train numbering over a hundred. In 1843 there were 875 men, women and children who struggled to Oregon in ox-drawn wagons. From then until completion of the transcontinental railroad in 1869 it has been estimated that between a quarter and a half million emigrants took the Oregon Trail west.

The advent of coast-to-coast rail service did not stop travel over the Oregon Trail and in fact, wagon emigrants continued to use this route until the automobile made wagons obsolete in the early 1900s.

These latter-day wagon emigrants, the subject of TRACES, found their trip west vastly different from that of the early travelers. Towns had been established along the way where supplies could be purchased. And slow steady oxen were replaced with teams of mules and horses. But the hardship of the Oregon Trail had not changed; 2,000 miles of unforgiving country.

The stories of the pioneers in TRACES are as they remember — looking back a lifetime.

The Nye Family

Although the Nye family is fictional the story of their crossing, set in the late 1870s, and of the life Joe Nye led out west is based in part on fact. Old diaries were used as information to get a day-to-day feel of the trail and reminiscences of still-living pioneers helped to develop the fictional characters.

The Nye family settled near the town of Grand Ronde which was established as an early day Indian reservation; Willamette Valley as well as coastal Indians were confined there.

Like a lot of men in Oregon, Joe Nye took a job in the woods. He devoted himself to logging and when he could no longer work he turned to the outdoors — fishing.

In the last chapter of TRACES Joe Nye returns to the Blue Mountains for the dedication of the Oregon Trail. The celebration at Meacham actually did occur and President Warren G. Harding was there in person to proclaim Meacham the Capitol of the United States for a day on July 3, 1923. The final chapter parallels the course of events at that well-attended celebration.

Story Reference — *Pages 7, 27, 57, 83, 113, 155, 189.*

Lulu Barton — 1886

Lulu Barton was born October 1, 1885, in Wichita, Kansas. After her father James was murdered, Lulu, along with her mother Mary, brother Leon, aunt Jo Skinner and Nye Burnett, left Wamego, Kansas, by wagon and traveled as far as Big Horn, Wyoming.

Lulu married a Montana cowboy, Lynn Barnes, and they ranched and farmed. Finally in 1947 Lulu boarded a steam train and came as far west as is possible, to Oregon.

At age 94 Lulu resides at Columbia Basin Nursing Home in The Dalles, Oregon.

Story Reference — *Page 22.*

Grace Byers — 1892

Grace Byers was born October 18, 1888, in Battle Creek, Nebraska. The Byers family included father Rolla, mother Lillie and son Arthur, who was four years older than Grace. They left Nebraska heading for Hillsboro, Oregon, in 1892.

Grace married John Thogerson March 15, 1911, and they had four children. Grace and John were married 62 years and when John died he was buried in Vancouver, Washington. Grace wanted to keep the family together so she purchased additional lots beside John and had their baby Donny's grave moved from Dufur. He will rest for eternity beside his parents.

At age 91 Grace is residing in an apartment in Battleground, Washington.

Story Reference — *Pages 48, 78, 126, 158.*

George Craig — 1889

George Craig was born October 18, 1883, in Scotts Bluff, Nebraska. The family included father Chester, mother Lydia and sister Jane.

Chester ran a stage line to support the family but the plain's weather was harsh and when he found one of his stages with the driver and passenger frozen and the four-mule team dead, still standing in the traces, he decided it was time to look for a home elsewhere. The mild climate of western Washington attracted him.

The Craigs came west in 1889 and took an eighty-acre homestead near Bremerton, Washington. The constant rain got to them and the following year they returned to Nebraska. The second trip west began in 1899, the Craigs working on farms and ranches as they came. Crossing the Blue Mountains to eastern Washington, the accident that destroyed George's wagon occurred. They returned to the last valley they had passed.

George settled on ground near Summerville, Oregon. In 1905 George married Lulu Dot. After more than sixty years of marriage she passed away and George was never quite the same. In 1974 he moved to Twin Fir retirement home in La Grande, Oregon.

George hoped he could make it to age one hundred. But that was not to be: he died August 10, 1979.

Story Reference — *Pages 74, 146, 181.*

Lola Kennedy and George Kennedy — 1900

Lola Kennedy was born October 31, 1887, and her brother George was born November 1, 1889. The Kennedy family, consisting of father William, mother Ora Bell and six children came to Oregon in 1900.

Seventy-four years after the crossing Lola wrote an account of the wagon trip; she said she wanted to preserve it for family history. Lola was married to the late Earl Culver for 37 years and at age 92 Lola resides in La Grande, Oregon.

George Kennedy, age 90, lives by himself in Elgin, Oregon. He splits his own wood and keeps the stoves fired in winter. In summer he likes to sit on his front porch and watch the occasional traffic on the street in front of his house.

"Two things I have always been sure of," George claims. "Since way back I knew I would see man walk on the moon. I didn't know how he would get there but I figured when he did he wouldn't have to prowl around in the dark. The other thing I am sure of is that I'll never die like a decent person ought, I'll get killed or something. That is my personal feeling but as far as that goes I don't really give a damn."

Story Reference — *Pages 24, 46, 124.*   Story Reference — *Pages 40, 108, 160.*

Mabel Jones — 1898

Mabel Jones was born June 20, 1890, in Hayes County, Nebraska. Her family included father Jackson, mother Lydia, sisters Lilly and Leolah and brothers Alma, Lawrence, Jack and Charley.

Jackson was a gypsy traveler, never satisfied with where they were living, and as a result moved his family here and there from one state to another. In 1898 he gave up on Nebraska after hearing of good land near Sunnyside, Washington, but the Jones family never made it that far. On the fourth day of August they landed in North Powder, Oregon, and that is where they stuck. Twice Jackson tried to return to Nebraska. The first time in 1909 he convinced the family to accompany him. They loaded the old wagon and went as far as Snake River before Dorothy, Alma's daughter, fell in the water and nearly drowned. They returned to North Powder. Once again, in 1921, Jackson tried to go back. This time he was stopped by a stroke. But for the rest of his days he talked about how happy he had been with reins in his hands and a hill in front of him.

Mabel was content in North Powder, met farmer George Myles at a "kitchen sweat" dance and was married in 1906.

After George died in 1953 Mabel continued to live at North Powder but at age 89 she moved to the La Grande Nursing Home where she is now living.

Story Reference — *Page 18.*

Zola Lawrence — 1896

Zola Lawrence was born October 28, 1892, in Goodland, Kansas. The Lawrence family, consisting of father John, mother Della, and Percy, a brother one year younger than Zola, came to Oregon in 1896. Accompanying them were grandparents Billy and Ellen Lawrence.

On August 2, 1911, which Zola said was the highlight of her life, she married logger Wayne Menear. The only picture Zola has of her husband in the woods shows him May 20, 1941, the day of the accident. Wayne stands beside the tree that dropped the widowmaker which nearly killed him.

Life changed for Zola and Wayne after the accident and until his death in 1964 at the age of 76 Wayne was not able to return to the woods as a logger.

At age 87 Zola is a resident at Cascade Manor in Lebanon, Oregon.

Story Reference — *Pages 52, 80, 178.*

Martha Macy — 1900

Martha Macy was born April 22, 1894, in Glenrock, Wyoming. Her family included father Charles, mother Addie, sister Nellie and brothers Clarence, Charlie and Willie.

They left Wyoming the first day of August 1900 in a wagon bound for Forest Grove, Oregon, and arrived the middle of October. Martha attended school until the 8th grade and then went to work on a farm, milking cows and tending the orchard. In 1913 she was married to logger Osmar Kirby and they moved to the Bend area where they ranched for 26 years. They had six children, three boys and three girls.

Osmar died, the ranch was sold and Martha moved to Tumalo where she lived in a town house. To fill the void without Osmar, Martha kept her hands busy. She crocheted and knit beautiful lace and afghans. The fifth day of January 1979 Martha passed away.

Story Reference — *Page 128.*

Blanche McGaughey — 1898

Blanche McGaughey was born April 19, 1885, in Effingham, Illinois. Her father was John T. McGaughey and when her mother died Blanche assumed some of the family responsibilities. The family included brothers Will and John and sisters Mary, Sara Jane, Matty and Flo.

The McGaugheys started west in 1898 and got as far as Oklahoma. The family stayed there for three years and then Blanche left and came to Pendleton, Oregon, by train. Blanche rode in the Pendleton Round-Ups of 1912 - 1915, winning the Cowgirl's Bucking Contest for the Championship of the Northwest in 1912. She also rode in the Calgary Stampede and with the famous touring rodeo, the Hundred-and-One.

Blanche and Ted Sammis were married in 1915.

The last horse Blanche owned was named Rocky and after Ted had died and the ranch was sold in 1952, the new owner said he did not want a hayburner on the place. He sold Rocky for dog food.

At age 94 Blanche resides at Columbia Basin Nursing Home in The Dalles, Oregon.

Story Reference — *Pages 42, 170.*

Lizzie Page — 1883

Lizzie Page was born on the Oregon Trail in Iowa in 1883, only a matter of days after her sister Bessie had died. The family included father Abner, mother Eveline, and daughters Carrie and Bessie. They started west in 1883.

In Weston, Oregon, Abner Page had only fifty cents left to his name so they stopped while he took a job plowing for wages. He had intended to take his family to the Willamette Valley but decided instead to stay in northeast Oregon, making homes in Elgin, Wallowa, Imbler, and La Grande.

Lizzie married Alfred Fuller June 27, 1909, in Imbler. They had two children, Audrie and Tom.

Alfred passed away in Gresham in 1952 and at age 96 Lizzie is a resident of Central Oregon Health Care Center in Redmond, Oregon.

Story Reference — *Pages 104, 140, 163.*

Minnie Pfannebecker — 1898

Minnie Pfannebecker was born February 14, 1895, and at the age of three came west from Buffalo, Missouri, with her parents, brothers Harry and Ed, and sisters Nanny and Ella.

In 1928 Minnie married Harry Gill and they began farming near Big Butte on the prairie outside Grangeville, Idaho.

The horse that Minnie loved so much, Dick, lived to be 27 years old before being destroyed.

Minnie's return to Montpelier with sisters Nanny and Ella was in 1973 and since then both sisters have passed away leaving Minnie as the sole survivor of their wagon trip west.

At age 85, Minnie and her husband Harry live in their home in Grangeville, Idaho.

Story Reference — *Pages 77, 149, 169.*

Clifton Ross — 1891

Clifton Ross was born September 29, 1881, and crossed from Nebraska to Brownsville, Oregon, in 1891 with his father, mother and one brother John, five years older than Clifton.

The Ross family was interested in Oregon because of the fruit industry. When they reached Brownsville Mr. Ross asked an orchardist how much the charge would be if he turned his family loose to eat all the apples they wanted.

The oddity of the Ross crossing was that they brought a top buggy. Before they left Nebraska Mr. Ross traded for a used top buggy and after his wife had driven it to Oregon Mr. Ross sold it.

Clifton married Carrie Prince July 29, 1908, and they had two children, Milo and Doryce. At age 98 Clifton is a resident of Friendsview Manor in Newberg, Oregon; he and his wife have been married 71 years.   Story Reference — *Pages 49, 148.*

Sedalia Rucker — 1906

Sedalia Rucker was born December 2, 1892, in Wallowa, Oregon. Her mother Lucinda died of typhoid in 1894 and her father died three years later. Lew and Ella Rinehart raised Sedalia. They were parents not only to her but to other children in need of a home. The name Rinehart is still revered in Wallowa County because of the influence of their friendly, generous nature.

In 1906 they crossed Oregon over the Oregon Trail. Not long after they arrived at the Yamhill farm, Sedalia had her accident with the horses in the corral; blood poisoning formed and doctors amputated her leg.

Sedalia married Bert Dexter May 29, 1910, in Yamhill County, Oregon. They moved shortly after and for the first few years of marriage lived in California. Then when the Rineharts decided to retire, Sedalia and Bert returned to work their farm.

In 1924 they moved to eastern Oregon and began all over. Bert died while they were living in Irrigon, and Sedalia, at age 87, is living in Hermiston Good Samaritan Care Center.

Story Reference — *Pages 142, 176.*

Savannah Smith — 1899

Savannah Smith was born April 13, 1887, in Seneca, Missouri. The Smith family, including father Martin Van Buren, mother Eva and seven children, left Missouri in 1899 and came west by wagon. They settled on Happy Ridge south of The Dalles, Oregon.

Savannah married Harry Lewis on April 24, 1907, and they had seven children. Harry passed away in 1965 and after he was gone Savannah had a hard time taking care of herself and remembering to take her medicine. At the age of 92 Savannah is residing at Columbia Basin Nursing Home in The Dalles, Oregon.

The homestead land on which the Smiths filed is now part of a state wildlife preserve. The State of Oregon purchased the Happy Ridge land from the Smiths and burned their old house. The wagon which brought the family west was parked in the field behind the house and over the years it rotted away until now there is no longer any trace of it.

Story Reference — *Pages 107, 166.*

Mae Stone — 1898

Mae Stone was born January 31, 1885, in Parsons, Kansas. Her family, including father Warren, mother Edith and a younger brother Harry, came to the Willamette Valley of Oregon in 1898.

The diary she wrote was begun at the time they intersected the Oregon Trail in Idaho. Her father had been mining in Nevada for several years but gave that up to become an Oregon farmer.

Mae married Will Putnam but he passed away during the influenza epidemic of 1918 leaving Mae to raise their three children, Neil, Edith and one-day-old William. In 1937 Mae married Mack Snedden, and at age 95 Mae is a resident of Cascade Manor in Lebanon, Oregon.

Story Reference — *Page 130.*

Art Illustrations — by Don Gray

Photographic Illustrations —
by Gildemeister

Sinar 4x5, Linhof 4x5, and Hasselblad cameras were used for all photography except the Antelope Buck which was done with a Nikon 35mm. Kodak Ektachrome Professional, Plus-X and Tri-X films were used for all illustrations. A grain texture screen was utilized for several views.

Writer — Rick Steber . . .

Rick, the master storyteller, was reared in the southern Oregon town of Bonanza and now makes his home in the foothills of the rugged Wallowa Mountains.

Western history has always fascinated Rick and for the past eight years he has made a profession of writing history. Along with his wife Kristi, Rick travels the back roads of the West in search of colorful characters. The stories gleaned from oldtimers find their way into the syndicated newspaper column "Oregon Country," magazine articles, as well as the recent book publications of RENDEZVOUS and the UNION CENTENNIAL ALBUM. A mainstream fiction novel is to be published soon and he is currently working on a historical novel. In researching TRACES, Rick spent five years locating the last of our pioneers and recording their stories. To get a personal feel of the trail he put a pack on his back and walked 450 miles, following still visible ruts of the Oregon Trail from Snake River to the symbolic end of the trail, The Dalles.

Artist — Don Gray . . .

Born within a stone's throw of the Oregon Trail in northeast Oregon's Grande Ronde Valley, Don's fascination with its history began at an early age. The opportunity to illustrate the stories in TRACES became for him a labor of love. To gain personal understanding and assure accuracy to detail he visited with the pioneers and traveled to story locations, spending much time in research and preliminary drawings before the final artwork was even begun.

A professional artist since the age of twenty-two, his paintings have been exhibited widely in galleries and museums throughout the United States.

Don lives on a small acreage near Union, Oregon, with his wife Brenda and children Heather, Melissa, and Jared.

Photographer — Jerry Gildemeister . . .

Photograph by Cathy Gildemeister

Jerry's long-time interest in western heritage drew him to the Blue Mountain area of the Oregon Trail over a quarter century ago. His forestry background transformed into a profession of photography and design which he shares with his wife, Cathy, in their studio-home located in the foothills of the Wallowa Mountains.

This opportunity to join Rick and Don in preserving the accounts of our last-living pioneers was met with great enthusiasm. He and Cathy traveled over 14,000 miles along the Oregon Trail to photographically set the mood of the long wagon trip westward. His photographic illustration in addition to project planning, book design, and overall production responsibility, filled out the talents necessary for the creation of these final days of the Oregon Trail — TRACES.

The Bear Wallow Publishing Company

TRACES is a joint effort of writer • Rick Steber, artist • Don Gray, and photographer • Jerry Gildemeister who have pooled their talents in this creative endeavor to preserve a part of our western heritage. To assure the highest artistic quality they chose to form their own publishing company . . . thus, The Bear Wallow.

Credits. . . .

TRACES was designed by — Jerry Gildemeister.

Manuscript preparation and editing by — Kristi Steber.

Final editing by — Jack Evans, Director of Libraries, E.O.S.C., La Grande, Oregon.

Color separations were prepared from the original artwork and transparencies by — Pacific Color Plate Company — Portland, Oregon.

Halftones were prepared from the original artwork and photographic prints by — Bob Foree, Baker Printing & Lithography — Baker, Oregon.

The text was set in Garamond No. 49 and No. 49 Italic by — L. R. Casteel Typesetting Co., Barbara Mingeaud, Connie Hasten and Leona Casteel, typesetters — Seattle, Washington.

The end sheet maps were set in Americana, Perpetua, and Snell Roundhand by — Portland Linotyping Company — Portland, Oregon.

The book was printed by — The Irwin Hodson Company — Portland, Oregon.

Stripping and plate preparation — Bob Koppler
Printing by —
Jerry Mickow, Head Pressman and Charles Oaks, Assistant.
28x40″ 2-color Heidleberg Offset.
Steve Borland, Head Pressman and Dave Getsinger, Assistant.
38″ 2-color Miehle Offset.
Bob Tallman — Pressman.
29″ Single-color Miehle Offset.
Pressroom inspection — Darwin Pindell.
Pressroom supervision — Don Turina

Paper was supplied by — Fraser Paper Company — Portland, Oregon.
The text paper is 100# White Optimum Dull
Manufactured by — Midtec Paper Corporation — Kimberly, Wis.
The end sheets are 65# Aged Parchment Cover
Manufactured by — French Paper Company — Niles, Mich.

Printing inks were PMS for accent and Process, supplied by — Cal/Ink — San Francisco, California.

The book was bound by — Lincoln & Allen Co. — Portland, Oregon.
The cover fabric is imitation leather by — Gane Bros. and Lane, Inc.

Production coordination was by — Gildemeister assisted by Cathy Gildemeister.

Library of Congress Cataloging in Publication Data

Steber, Rick, 1946–
    Traces.

Writing: R. Steber; artwork: D. Gray; photography and design: J. Gildemeister.
Includes index.
    SUMMARY: A fictional account of the Nye family's trek to Oregon accompanies narration written from interviews with some of the last surviving pioneers who actually traveled the Oregon Trail.
    1. Oregon Trail. 2. Overland journeys to the Pacific. 3. Pioneers — The West — Biography. 4. The West — Biography. 5. Frontier and pioneer life — The West. (1. Oregon Trail. 2. Overland journeys to the Pacific. 3. Frontier and pioneer life — The West. 4. Pioneers. 5. The West — Biography) I. Gray, Don, 1948 — II. Gildemeister, Jerry, 1934 — III. Title.

F597.S78   917.8′042   80-11339

Traces — ISBN-0-936376-02-3

— Other Publications by The Bear Wallow —

RENDEZVOUS, First Printing, © 1978. ISBN-0-936376-00-7.
RENDEZVOUS, Second Printing, © 1978. ISBN-0-936376-01-5.

We dedicate this book to those who still remember.